'Pear Nuallak's critiq[...] is expansive. Their essay[...] only really come from [...]ce between the cruelties of the world we have and the possibilities of the worlds we can make. Their vision is verdant, their wit is wondrous, and their hope calls us home.'
— Harry Josephine Giles, author of *Deep Wheel Orcadia*

'*Pearls from Their Mouth* is a lighthouse—both a warning signal and a safe harbour, telling us that the first step towards dismantling the social conditions predetermined by racial capitalism is the unapologetic rejection of it all. A sharp and stunning queer offering, there to be worn like a charm.'
— Heba Hayek, author of *Sambac Beneath Unlikely Skies*

'A nourishing ode to the uncontainable; a generous, incisive call to get close to the body, texture and raw material of how we build another world together.'
— Remember & Resist

'Pear Nuallak moves with purpose into the complex knot of life as a diasporic Thai queer in Britain, not to unravel it into digestible narrative but to find a way of feeling out the tensions stretched along its many strands. A remarkable book.'
— the right lube

'In both their essays and fictional stories, Pear communicates with a refreshing and rare degree of radical honesty, breaking down all the uncomfortable internal and external barriers that we face in social justice spaces. This book feels like an essential read for anyone fighting, or wanting to fight, for collective liberation.'
— June Bellebono, transfeminine writer, organiser and founder of *oestrogeneration*

'A deeply thought-provoking, tender and exquisitely written collection. Pear has the extraordinary ability to incisively critique multiple power structures at once, whilst also balancing this with hopeful urgency. Their generous offering is a must-read for anyone who is looking to create change in increasingly precarious, dark times.'
— Maymana Arefin, a.k.a. @fungi.futures

'Pear Nuallak both dismantles the world around us and reimagines it. By blending essays and fiction in incisive and lyrical prose, they create an utterly unique experience that is both revelatory and thrilling. A dazzling read.'
— Akil Kumarasamy, author of *Meet Us by the Roaring Sea*

PEARLS FROM
THEIR MOUTH

First published in the United Kingdom in 2022
by Hajar Press C.I.C.
www.hajarpress.com
@hajarpress

ISBN 978-1-914221-14-9 Paperback
ISBN 978-1-914221-15-6 EPUB eBook

A Cataloguing-in-Publication data record for this book is available
from the British Library.

Cover and interior art: Hanna Stephens
Cover design: Samara Jundi
Typesetting: Laura Jones / lauraflojo.com

Printed and bound in the United Kingdom by
Clays Ltd, Elcograf S.p.A.

PEARLS FROM THEIR MOUTH

PEAR NUALLAK

I offer this book to my loved ones

To those who burn with anger they want neither
to be engulfed by nor to swallow down

To every person who understands that we can
always choose a different starting point

Contents

PLAYLIST

Lingua Ignota – 'God Gave Me No Name (no Thing Can Hide from My Flame)'

Guayaba – 'Mariposa Mala'

Mitski – 'Shame'

Scarling. – 'Bummer'

SOPHIE – 'Faceshopping'

Rina Sawayama – 'Comme Des Garçons (Like The Boys)'

The Birthday Massacre – 'Video Kid'

Brooke Candy – 'Opulence'

Bauhaus – 'She's In Parties'

The Southern Death Cult – 'Moya'

Japanese Breakfast – 'Boyish'

Backxwash – 'DONT COME TO THE WOODS'

Lupa Lari – 'teeth'

Mitski – 'Stay Soft'

Peter Andre – 'Mysterious Girl'

Rina Sawayama – 'Fuck This World (Interlude)'

Big Momma – 'Dentata'

Allie X feat. Mitski – 'Susie Save Your Love'

Hozier – 'NFWMB'

Mitski – 'A Pearl'

Emma Ruth Rundle & Thou – 'Out of Existence'

Amy Winehouse – 'In My Bed'

INTRODUCTION

This is a book about the body—not the sacrosanct or safe or enfleshed body, but all the strange, gorgeous, sensate forms that experience the world.

This is a book about desire where nobody gets what they think they want.

This is a book about power, which nobody understands how much or how little they have.

There are stories and there are essays; I have put them together because I was allowed to. I can't really write flowing prose anymore, but maybe we're all post-lengthy attention span these days, and I believe in trying to meet people where they are.

*

If you're reading this book to feel seen and represented, to find the soothingly relatable in my words, characters and ideas, ask yourself why you think I could give this to you, or to anyone. I would like to draw your attention away from your image in the eyes of another and instead to your mouth, which is filled with teeth. It is never too late to learn to bite the hand that feeds.

*

Everything I have written has come from conversations I have had with loved ones who are more interesting, knowledgeable and experienced than me. Even before the pandemic I found it difficult to go outside, and I have never organised anything more complicated than a craft evening. These words were all born of my friends and communities, and I write them because I like to and can type like a demon, not necessarily because I'm any good.

This book would not exist without Hajar Press, who created a context for me to place my work and tended to it with great care and patience.

*

I wrote this in the final year of my art degree, and in some ways, it is a record of the inquiries I am making in my artistic practice. It's very difficult to actually work as an artist. The artworld relies on individualism and fierce competition alongside an aesthetic of artists-as-radical-working-class, all amidst real, ongoing labour struggles by artists against conditions of shocking exploitation and precarity. This book's title comes from a Facebook post that I shared on 3 March 2021 expressing my cynicism on this subject:

> i think sometimes tutors know they're being annoying, as if their irritating comments are the apocryphal grit that ultimately results in a pearl formed within the soft insides of young artists. but the thing that actually prompts a pearl is a parasite, or damage to the shell, or actually, fuck this analogy, because i'm not going to be slit open and divested of something that is essentially commoditised scar tissue.

> all of this so that you can be trained into someone just as annoying as them, a fucking clown who generates objects that are collected as investments for the ruling class, or petitions the state for money to blunder into local communities while pantomiming radicalism. the latter generates cultural rather than financial capital, both provide entertainment for the ruling class.

I don't want to feel like this. Making art is important to me, but artists are annoying ... so what does that make me? I enjoy art so much but find I seem to treat my own emotions like a distasteful joke just so I'm not put in the same box as those scabs who wankily over-theorise their own cowardice.

Art should be action, a way of forming relationships with each other, a way of anticipating new worlds and testing ideas for liberation. If we don't want art to be an aesthetic repository for rich people's money, we have to claw it back.

I am not willing to give up on art altogether. It won't save us, but art is one more thing we can do together.

*

The movement of my grandparents and my parents across borders, their decisions for survival, their determination to chase their dreams, have in turn created a dream in me—not a hope or an ambition, but something that arrives each night to choke me in my bed. When I sleep, I see an English rose garden swallowed in mud that oozes around a decaying home, where, in my childhood bedroom, I squeeze myself into dolls' dresses. My hair, which I keep fastidiously shaved in waking life, shoots out from my scalp, amassing itself until my neck cannot possibly support such weight. I am always alone. It is rare for me to dream of anything else; when I do, it is usually, thankfully, about friends or important moments in the waking world that will require me to act.

I tell you this to show you that my dreams, the dreams of individuals, have no value. When I speak of dreaming a future, I mean something awake and shared, alive with possibilities.

*

ONE

ON IMAGES OF
DEATH AND LOVE

I write this in March 2022 after the first anniversary of the Atlanta shootings, in which a white American man went on a killing spree across spas and massage parlours in Georgia's capital city. Eight lives were taken, including those of six Asian women. In my hands I thumb a smooth stone of grief, turning it over and over, and it is because I am holding this stone that I can speak more slowly.

In a few pages, I will explain why real anti-racism demands that we push through the neat, slick promises of conventional 'representation' into something else. But before breaking down arguments, facts and methods, I would like to offer you feeling—emotional reactions to the world—as this is where many of us begin.

In popular imagery, Asian people are frequently associated with non-human technologies—robots that can labour endlessly; clever, immortal machines; pretty dolls that never tire and, if broken, are always replaceable. Food, healing, sex: these are our uses. We are made for export, a resource required to maintain the lifestyles of 'real' humans, yet so productive that we threaten to extinguish them.

Here, something else crawls underneath the imagery's shining surface. Asians are also compared to vermin and viruses, constantly swelling in number. This sensuousness, contagion, mass collectivity—the perpetual expansion of our ornamentation and corruption—must be kept under control.

The uniform of domination can be worn by anyone willing to bear the cost: the spree killers, serial attackers, soldiers and police officers that serve as white supremacy's striking arm. Under this system, we are made to be used and discarded, controlled and eliminated.

To push against this imagery, Asians have tried to point out that we too are human, all flesh and feelings that can be hurt. Above all, we insist on our innocence, civility and capacity for sacrifice. We ignore that the cost of our claim to innocence is its presumption of another's criminality. To question innocence would destroy the mode of respectable citizenship that we have worked so hard to invent and inhabit; it is the imagery that we ourselves brandish as evidence that our wounds are not deserved.

Each killing, each missing person, each injured Asian body is unbearably painful. We are afraid. We believe that the danger is rooted in our 'identity', which means we are all equally unsafe, which means any one of us could be next. We embrace the framework of 'hate crime' and its offers of protection; we call for more prosecutions, more police. We've heard the arguments that police are bad, but no one knows our desperation, that we can never let this happen again, no matter the cost ... We lay the arguments aside for later, deciding that freedom is a fair sacrifice for full enjoyment of the state's love.

Maybe people cannot think of freedom as anything but a cold, empty, English sky, so anything that calls itself love is preferable. But bell hooks teaches us about love that holds injustice to account, love that actually stands for something, love against domination, offering clarity, warmth and knowledge to the subjugated and unrelenting scrutiny of the systems that oppress us. There's more to loving our families and communities than cut-up fruit and linear histories, silent service and sacrifice. What good is love that does not urge, push, move, transform?

Perhaps some will say that I am Westernised and that Asian love is quiet, subtle, full of small details. I say, have you never faced the fury of a parent, bursting forth or freezing you out, the purity of their rage wielded against you in punishment, and thought:

*I wish you showed me this **intensity** in tenderness instead*
???

If love is in the details, then I want to know everything. I want to know about what power does to love, working inter-generational trauma into our families so we do not embrace and lift one another but grip each other tightly in fear. And I want to know about what love can do to power, how we can repair and extinguish any possibility of harm. I am so hungry for love like this. I hope you are, too.

*

REPRESENTASIAN
MYTHOLOGIES (1)

The project of liberation is being hollowed out by the shallow politics of representation. We are told that ESEAs—the latest acronym for East and South-East Asians—need to fight for recognition, visibility, inclusion, access to the corridors of power. Don't be fooled: radical change isn't forged when some exploited people are made into heroes and channelled into higher positions within the very same exploitative systems. This trick is being pulled in the arts as in politics; under capitalism, powerful institutions—whether big film companies or governments—have the will and the means to neutralise growing resistance, violently repressing it and then speedily extracting its *style*, its potential, distilled and rendered palatable, rebranded as something new, fresh, invigorating. We must always be alert and responsive to this ruse. We must attack the system from every possible angle, not feed more people into its belly.

These might seem like strange declarations. After all, hasn't there been an increase in public awareness about racism in recent years? Isn't radical change already happening? Amid global Black abolitionist uprisings and the Covid pandemic, the #StopAsianHate UK campaign emerged in the early 2020s promising to fight racism against Asians in Britain by raising money for grassroots ESEA organisations. The movement has a high media profile, driven by support from several prominent actors, journalists, influencers and suchlike. Agitation by Asians in these sectors for 'better ESEA representation' isn't particularly surprising—it would benefit them. Maybe this framing seems uncharitable, but it's important to examine how—and in whose interests—the push for representation came to dominate our discussions about oppression before we make such demands the cornerstone of our activism.

While celebrities were shaping popular discourse around racism, numerous ESEA activist groups also formed in 2020–2021. In the UK, these include besea.n, Southeast and East Asian Centre, and End Violence and Racism Against ESEA Communities. There is a genuine spirit of camaraderie among these groups; they work alongside each other and with established organisations that have been providing vital services for East and South-East Asian migrant communities for decades, such as Hackney Chinese Community Services and Kanlungan Filipino Consortium. These organisations—and this list is by no means exhaustive—coordinate a huge range of events that encompass everything from protests to group forest walks to hate crime workshops.

Any work that brings together people who have been isolated and under-served is worthwhile. I worry, though, about the tendency to think history could move along a bright and obvious path to a big pot of freedom, and that new ways of grouping people illuminate the way forward on this path. What does all this mean for the ways we try to serve our communities?

*

I wish to acknowledge that my younger self would have found the current ESEA movement and its demands for representation truly ground-breaking. I grew up in 1990s–2000s Croydon in South London. Like many in Asian diasporas, I first began to understand race through asking questions about skin and celebrity. Why did people make uncomfortable comments about my appearance? Why did they insist on remarking on the size, shape and smell of my home, my food and my body? Why weren't there any public figures who looked like me—did

I even exist outside of people's weird fantasies? How could I make sense of the fact that paleness is idealised in Thai culture when I was surrounded by white girls who, with the exception of grungers and emos, all thickly coated themselves in self-tanning lotion? And why did no one seem to care about the indignities my family and I experienced every day?

I resented being told that such concerns were superficial; after all, these were daily encounters or erasures that affected me immediately on an emotional level. They would form part of my psychological landscape. In this context, seeing more ESEA representation—knowing that people 'like me' could take up our own space, tell our own stories, thrive, be seen and admired—would have felt very good. The emotion of recognition is potent; it *feels* like something substantial, even if it isn't.

Contrary to certain narratives about ESEA families, my parents were very open about their feelings and highly artistic. I emphasise this because 'expressing feelings' and 'doing more art' are things I have frequently seen being proposed as strategies for ESEA community care. But expressiveness and art aren't intrinsically transformative; the context in which they happen matters. Arguably, bringing people into a communal space where they can form bonds with one another is the most important thing here. Well, to do that, you need a venue. Do you have funding and the skills to set up a welcoming, accessible and smoothly run space, with facilitators, materials, food and drink? A transport budget for attendees wouldn't go amiss, either. What I'm trying to say is, feeling isn't everything. The practical stuff—the material—matters.

When I was growing up, what would have made the most meaningful difference to my family was secure housing, followed closely by support in asserting our rights as tenants and workers and in demanding even more. Free, long-term, high-quality English classes, culturally considerate mental health support, and a local community centre serving the needs of South-East Asian communities—all in place as permanent provisions, free from bidding cycles for renewed funding—would also have been incredible. But this isn't how things work in Britain, where the neoliberal project—characterised by the expansion of the logic of free-market capitalism to all aspects of human life—has gutted the welfare state, privatised everything and offered us policing in the place of care. The truth is that life-affirming resources should not be prizes to be won in competition or privileges to be removed in punishment; nor should they be serviced by the state's desire to surveil and criminalise its population.

It would not have helped my family if more people in the class of bosses and landlords exploiting us had been Asian. The core myth of representation politics is that someone who looks like you and shares your cultural touchstones will naturally advocate for your shared interests. They *feel* relatable. And while the force of this imagined affinity exerts a powerful emotional pull, the ever-present power imbalance goes unseen.

*

The mythology of ESEA discourse goes something like this:

Nobody cares about our struggles. We're a minority within a minority. Racism against ESEAs *in particular* has always been normalised, and it has become even worse because of Covid, Trump, Boris Johnson and Brexit.

We face discrimination because of how our 'identity' is maligned. We are invisible yet also seen as servile or sexualised. Well, some of us don't work at takeaways, we're middle managers! How *dare* people assume we're the nanny when we're the wife?

We are being targeted by hate crime, and no one cares. The newspapers don't report the killings of our elders and the police don't help us when we're assaulted and abused (media coverage and police protection being very important community resources).

It feels as though we're screaming and no one is paying attention.

Luckily for us, there's a blueprint for combatting all this anti-ESEA hate. All we need to do is break down the walls of indifference with education; follow half a dozen ESEA community groups, celebrities and influencers on social media; increase positive ESEA representation; support ESEA businesses; welcome police into our communities and report hate crime; collect lots and lots of data; work nicely with the government; and speak up when people do racism against us, which covers everything from wearing fox-eye make-up to passing us over for promotion to battering us in the street.

Importantly, we must also fund the revolution. We can #StopAsianHate by donating to self-described anti-racist ESEA organisations, without looking too closely at who they are, what their money is used for, or whether lesser-known groups might have a stronger track record of providing vital services without the same attention or fanfare. These questions don't really matter, because we're all in this together, and ultimately, it's all for the good of the community. Right?

*

You are beginning to sense more than a little contempt here, perhaps.

I confess, I cannot join this new ESEA movement, since I find it aesthetically and politically repugnant. There is a corporate gloss on all the campaigns, reports and posts I see, influencer-infographic slickness thickly poured over the sharp edges of trauma and humiliation, a nice twenty-slide deck that promises to make white people better 'allies' afterwards.

I want to ask some of these activists: where is your anger? Where is the fire? Where are the teeth? What are you actually *doing*, and what do you actually want? Do you need someone else to tell you it's okay just to say, ***FUCK THIS SHIT***?

For all its revolutionary gestures, this movement remains an essentially neoliberal project. To the RepresentAsian activists, the problem is not capitalism but rather that ESEAs do not feature more prominently among the higher rungs of its hierarchy. I do not want to live within a hierarchical power structure at all. Demands for carcerality—for the expansion of police powers and its presence in our community—are also disturbingly strong in this movement. I want a future with no prisons.

Despite the effort that has gone into making a visually beautiful and emotionally compelling case for cultural unity, when it comes down to it, we are dreaming of very different worlds.

*

The central focus of RepresentAsian activism is to increase ESEA visibility. Middle-class ESEAs often grumble that they are either invisible or seen through 'negative stereotypes', rudely assumed to be lowly 'menial' labourers like cleaners, nannies and workers in food service, massage parlours or nail salons. ESEAs who engage in sex work, sell illegal goods or lack immigration documents—in other words, those at the sharpest edge of oppression—only give more fodder to harmful stereotypes about us and should be dealt with through criminalisation. Healthcare work is the single occupation seen as worthy, although these workers don't necessarily reap any actual benefits from the lauding of their vocation—this is especially true of undocumented Filipino migrants who have been pressured to work in extremely risky conditions during the pandemic.[1] Work is understood as an expression of an individual's moral position: good work is its own reward, bad work its own punishment, and if you fail to better yourself, it's your own fault.

This narrative rests on the idea that power comes from moving up a hierarchy, rather than being built at its base. To many ESEAs, working-class and migrant struggles serve just one purpose: they can be milked for appeals to whiteness for social mobility. Tell your experience of hate crime to get people to take you seriously; tell your family's story of poverty to qualify for a diversity scheme. Often you don't have a choice; regurgitating stories of suffering seems to be part of the process to access any kind of support, whether it be a bursary, deadline extension, therapy, social housing or asylum. I want you no longer to see this as natural, as just how things are. I want you to notice the cramp and the strain.

A constant flow of trauma stories isn't actually necessary to administrate basic resources, and it wears us into a certain shape. It means that the vital therapeutic act of disclosing our pain, expressing our core human need to be listened to, becomes enmeshed with being deemed worthy of support by charities and state institutions. It means that we cede a lot of ground to these institutions and accept humanity on terms offered by them. We are prompted to say, 'We're human too!' without pausing to consider how every word in that sentence is absurd, how we have been forced to become complicit in our own dehumanisation, performing our abjection, begging for scraps from the powerful.

*

The term 'ESEA' is not new, but its recent usage charges it with new political meaning, and I would like to scrutinise it more closely. The acronym is presented as an attempt to build solidarity beyond specific ethnic groups. Diana Yeh describes 'British East and Southeast Asian' as a political category that has been mobilised by cultural workers, particularly members of non-profit organisation BEATS (British East Asians in the Theatre and on Screen).[2] 'ESEA' pushes back against the monolith of 'Chineseness' and the stereotype of the model minority while also supposedly being more accurate than 'Other Asian'—and all without reminders of the fraught history that resounds in sickly terms like 'Oriental' and 'yellow'.

The idea that 'ESEA' hits the sweet spot of being inclusive *and* accurate *and* self-identified is interesting. For one thing, it takes geographical bounds as objective and neutral facts, when of course there is nothing more violent or contested than territories and their borders. For another, 'East and South-East Asia' might best be understood as an area in the West's political imagination where communist countries threaten capitalist hegemony. Neither of these considerations have featured within the given reasons for the label's political significance. The outright rejection of 'yellow' and 'Oriental' as organising terms because they are seen as particularly and intrinsically racist also misses the reason for the existence of any racial nomenclature in the first place, which is to forcefully divide people into differentiated categories of labour under imperialism. By organising under these terms, anti-racist activists can evoke the violence of imperialism and build solidarity to resist it.

In truth, there doesn't seem to be much of an idea of what 'race' actually is. Sometimes it is understood as a shared phenotypic register, with a focus in ESEA discourse on topics like beauty standards and desirability, and on how people become targets for hate crime because they are visibly read as Chinese. However, the term 'ESEA' is not just used to describe people who are racialised in uniform ways—indeed, part of its adopters' intention is to push back against the notion that Asians all look the same. In advocating this umbrella acronym and its variousness, they teeter on the cusp of admitting the instability and fluidity of race, before falling back on the belief that all we need is better, more accurate, more respectful terminology to describe our racial category. Because if we can just correctly name our race and become legible to the system, if we can get it to use the right words for us, then maybe we can finally access its riches ...

In this framework, freedom will be reached not through the destruction of borders, prisons and nation states, but rather through reform, diversity and inclusion—an approach proven to be ineffectual and hollow. 'Ethnic minority' elites have always been part of the imperialist machine; they were educated at Oxbridge and SOAS both during and after formal British rule, before being installed in high positions in colonial and neo-colonial governments.[3] It is very doubtful that the 'native' working classes were thrilled to share a 'race' with the people oppressing them, or that they were shown any particular mercy because of ethnic solidarity.

Those who advocate 'ESEA unity' seem to have forgotten these histories, as well as the unequal distribution of power and resources today. But until we recognise that dismantling racism requires the destruction of all structures of oppression, we'll never arrive at a truly anti-racist framework for our activism.

*

As much as ESEA activist groups insist that we have the same common interests because of our identities, our political goals are at stark odds. Reading each of their mission statements is deeply alienating and, if you will excuse the loaded pun, *disorientating*. There is an incoherence and dissonance in their aims: while many of these organisations have pushed for more police officers and the expansion of laws against hate crime as measures that would benefit ESEA people, the same groups also support #KillTheBill protests *against* legislation to ramp up police powers. Even their supposed community-based solutions to harm, such as third-party services for reporting racist violence, often link with the police. It's as though they think that policing just needs to be harnessed for good, which demonstrates a serious misunderstanding of both the purpose of policing and the reality of police violence in marginalised communities. In their desire for selectively effective authoritarianism, these groups seek not the destruction of the carceral state but accommodation within it, which makes me wonder why they even bother to attempt to frame themselves as part of a global anti-racist struggle. They frequently deploy words like 'care' and 'solidarity' that imply mutual relationships, all while believing that the state should wield the power to imprison and brutalise people—just the right ones, in the right ways.

It's one thing to acknowledge that we're obliged to make constrained choices to survive under racial capitalism; quite another to dream of a revolution that will merely bring a more successful version of neoliberalism. Those mobilising within the ESEA framework hide their reformist political vision and attachment to the punitive state and its hierarchies under the guise of progressiveness that comes with asserting their 'diasporic culture'.

I do not propose that we drop the political category of 'ESEA'; the problem isn't terminology. Call them what they like—it won't stop some people yearning for more power and more prisons. We could yearn for liberation instead.

*

FIFTH FINGER, LEFT HAND

I'm a *GIRL* today, and my mind is a tight-spined book, my memories words that creep too close to the gutter. I lean on the pages with my full weight, but I can never quite crease open the seam and understand what's written.

It is in notes and clippings that I've tried to capture my sister. When she sees my box of notebooks, Auntie Somruay sucks her teeth.

'It's upsetting, child, to see you persist,' she says, twisting the corner of her chemise. She took us in when we first appeared in Chang Thong village. My detective work is considered an eccentric habit. 'Years ago, you wanted a ring. You woke up and cried, pointing to the little finger of your left hand, insisting I help you find it. You dreamed it was lost and wouldn't accept that it had never existed. Do you remember?'

She shuffles into the kitchen without waiting for my answer. But the fact of a sister can neither be imagined nor dreamed.

*

The woman knew two things as she approached Lopamudra's office: memories are precious, and witches are efficient. Their work is beautiful economy; any tech bro can chin-strokingly commodify human relationships into a string of numbers, but witches have *style*. They do not concern themselves with speculation, watching whether lines go up or down and hoping monetary wealth might materialise, but deal directly with their resources—memories, dreams, wishes, power—assessing value according to ancient, immutable laws that have existed for uncountable ages. Provided your willingness to pay the price, a competent witch could take anything from you and transform it into anything in return, and she would do so with such an attractive, symbolic resonance, such glamour and poetry, that you'd be grateful for her singing blade even if you were the one being sliced open and bled dry.

Windows twice the woman's height showed a city the hue of dirt and all the shades of misery. London. It was nothing like the frank city blocks, red earth and scrubby mountains of Khorat. The witch's office existed between planes, accessible only to those who could navigate interstices—a form of client screening, said Lopamudra, since one could never be too discerning. In Himmapan, her building took the form of a curious whitewashed structure that hung like a bat on the underside of a cliff; in London, it was a black cube suspended between the fire escapes of two red-brick buildings.

Inside, the witch was carefully painting her nails the perfect colour of poison.

'You again.' Lopamudra gestured towards a plush leather chair by her black glass desk. The client seated herself with languorous ease before uttering a proposal of finely balanced magic that dangled in the air with the stench of solvents.

Lopamudra simply admired the glossy nails of her splay-fingered hand. Then, she lunged like a snake, leaning over the desk, belly to glass, poised as if to kiss.

'I've always found your audacity rather attractive,' she said. 'You'd do well with a wife of iron will and strong thighs.'

'Do we have an agreement? You know I deliver.' The client's true voice was crow-harsh. She leaned back and flicked a hair from her pale trench coat.

Lopamudra laughed, shaking her head from side to side, her bob swinging. 'How could I forget our first deal? I was still an optimistic rshika and you a princess of Krailat. The loss of your ability to fly between worlds was a fair trade for your desires. Those were such pretty green and gold wings ... Tell me, how long has it been since you last saw your little sister?'

The movements flitting across her client's face brought pleasure to the witch, juicy as durian. What Lopamudra particularly desired was misery; in all her deals and proceedings, she skimmed pain and suffering off the top like cream, licking it from her fingers, letting it slide down her throat. This client was making her very hungry.

'But that's why you've come to me,' she continued. 'You want to cross realms like rishi but with the bold step of a witch. You find honesty in these transactions, and you're willing to pay like no other.'

The client settled back in her chair with crossed arms. 'So, we have a deal?'

Lopamudra smoothed the front of her tailored dress. 'You know, Ploy, I've always wondered why you fetter yourself to others in the hope you'll escape yourself—but *that* part is none of my business. Shall we begin?'

Ploy handed her a thick stack of memories. 'My deposit for sister and sanctuary.'

'Yes,' Lopamudra murmured, 'that should cover it.' She shivered in anticipation. Memories caused the most exquisite pain, churned up desires beyond what people felt was possible. 'But you realise that for the Sanctuary to continue in the way you wish, you will need to regularly extract the memories of its inhabitants, stabilising the space through the amortisation of their suffering, or else find a way to release your guests once the payment has been fully settled?'

'Of course.'

The witch smiled, delighted. 'Then, we have a deal.'

The first things Lopamudra ate were Ploy's two wedding days, one at the registry office, one at the Wimbledon temple. Then came her little sister's memories: a photo of a child in cotton pyjamas, with gappy teeth and black hair tied up like a fountain;

another of a youth in white and blue, Bata shoes and a scowl, bent over a Game Boy in the dappled shade of a ficus tree.

Lopamudra's scissors chirped through photo paper. She turned the strips in a clay dish filled with a powder that might have been chilli salt but for its opalescent shimmer, then tidily swallowed each piece.

Lastly, there was a pile of cut-up paper. Lopamudra breathed in. Each word lifted from the page, serifs unsticking, tiny letters streaming into her mouth like winged termites. Yantras and dotted lines blossomed on the blank space left behind; she added her signatures and ate the lot, inhaling deeply through her nose as her jaw stretched beyond human capacity. The payment was taken. Lopamudra drew her fork and spoon together, satisfied.

*

I know I had an older sister, though I have no memory of her face; the idea of her is only a faint stain on the fabric of my recall.

When I think of my childhood, the following things appear:

1. my home, Chang Thong, with its full complement of rangy bantams, pickup trucks and internet cafes;
2. Auntie Somruay and her catfish curry;
3. teachers I hated, snitching classmates, laughing with friends;
4. at age thirteen, my first mobile phone (Samsung, silver) and first kiss (Emmy, room 3).

At least, I think her name was Emmy. Everyone knows an Emmy.

I'm sure I told someone at home about that kiss. I can still see a tiny ring glittering on the fifth finger of that someone's left hand as she gestured, a low laugh humming through skin-warmed fabric pressed tight against my cheek. It can't have been Auntie … she loathes hugs and costume jewellery, and I can never be sure how she feels about my being a tom.

When I sift my recollections, instead of my sister's image on the back of my eyelids, I see the man who took her: tall, pale, eyes blue and harsh as stove flames. After that, all I have are memories of missing someone, of looking for her in my face or gestures or lilting voice, crying with frustration when I come up empty each time.

I grow sick of trying to figure it out through my own body, so I become a detective in the formidable outfit of GIRL.

(Well, Auntie told me to be GIRL.)

Villages like mine usually bristle with stories, narratives colliding and interrupting one another in gossipy enthusiasm. Since old women see and remember everything, I approach the village's most feared and most beloved snack vendor. I should have understood that Grandma Fried Taro offers only two things: exceptional deep-fried foods and hot, fresh insults. She is legendary, frowning over black oil and sweet batter, cursing people two generations into their past and two into their future if they bother her with small talk.

After asking for my usual fried snack, I chance it. 'Grandma, please could I ask … my sister, Ploy—'

Her head snaps up. Her mouth opens. She has a voice like a chainsaw, and I run.

Other villagers are charmed by how I come to them: immaculate school sailor suit, braid like a hornet sting, a disguise that says GIRL. Despite my efforts, I find these usually voluble grandmas, aunties, cousins and sisters have astonishingly little to say. Once I pose the question, I can see each person thinking, a whirr of thought like a beetle fanning its wings, but the answers die on their lips every time. People stumble over sentences and turn, confused, back to their books and tablets. They mumble things about my sister being a tall, rough-voiced woman called Phim or Muk or Soi, who apparently had as many personalities as she did names: she was kind but irascible, cold but gentle. No one possesses a single picture of her or knowledge of where she went.

Still, I never tire of asking questions. They never tire of forgetting to answer. I work on the village from mathayom to mahalai. When I am old enough to know about bureaucracy, I flit in and out of offices, only to be presented with apologies and wrinkled foreheads, records wiped or corrupted or non-existent. Internet searches yield profiles of suspiciously near-identical young women who never quite fit the bill.

The only person I can't question is Auntie Somruay. Something is up; she feigns ignorance or bursts into tears if approached. I couldn't hurt my auntie, even if she's dissembling.

What I seek is not just proof of my sister's existence but any memory of her—us—with others, and I am denied at every turn.

*

One May morning, Grandma Fried Taro finally shuts up shop to live with grandnieces farther east.

'E nang,' she calls, 'come here.' She lies in her hammock as muscular women shift boxes around her. 'You asked about your sister, Ploy. I've got something to give you.'

'What is it, Grandma?'

'I never forget a face, not least some fool standing there with no shirt on in the midday sun, looking like the biggest motherfucking slice of naem I've ever seen. I slapped my forehead, exclaiming over my misfortune, and he saw it as an invitation and plodded towards me!' She strikes her knee grimly. 'That's farang for you: they think wen kam means *welcome*. He left this.'

I flick through vanity-published pulp. From this book, I learn the following:

1. my sleepy village can be transformed into something seedy and backwards, bristling with guns and machetes;

2. stories about strong-jawed white men saving brown women from brown men are interesting to the author;
3. on the back cover, Steve, a pink face with a sort-of nose, says he's thankful to his wife, Ploy, and keen to hear from readers;
4. Steve's email address.

It's easy to keep tabs on him over the years. I plot patiently.

When I tell Auntie Somruay that I want to go to England for university, she simply nods. 'We have savings. Just study hard.'

I stare. If we have that kind of money, why do we live in a modest little house? And what about getting a visa? What about all the things that make it impossible for everyone but the rich kids to go abroad? 'Don't worry about it, child,' Auntie says.

Her words send my body whirling forwards through time, like turning an electric mixer to full speed. I remember my hands, mostly, signing forms and writing exam answers and gesturing and greeting and thanking, room after room in flashing scenes, offices that look and smell the same but fulfil different functions in the complex arrangements that, eventually, somehow, lob me across the land and sea onto the island we call Angrit. I have no memory of saying goodbye to anyone; all I remember is sitting in the middle of my new bedroom, hemmed in by luggage.

My arrival in London is very straightforward. I know what I'm here for and what I'm meant to do. I start my course at university and take a job at the Thai restaurant frequented by my long-lost sister's ex-husband. I add *THAI* to my *GIRL* uniform for work, which means:

1. nice hair (I buy wigs from online cosplay stores);
2. smiling at racist jokes;
3. a very pretty little tilt of the head;
4. just a touch of make-up.

I need to be prepared.

Every Tuesday, I email Auntie. I have never yet received a reply.

*

The moment I see Steve, I know.

That lean frame with a doughy face slung on top, the voice delivered chiefly through the nostrils.

It's my first week at the restaurant. My co-worker steps forward, but I gently touch her sleeve. 'I'll take this one, Oil.'

'You sure, younger sister? He's a regular, but ... not the kind you want.'

'I'm sure.'

My hand shakes on the countertop as something inside me unknots, a memory freeing itself. He is the one who took her, this man as tall as a pret and just as eager to consume. A hungry, expectant look on his face as he gives me the once-over.

I smile, cooing approvingly as he mangles the names of dishes.

Weeks of deadlines, seminars and evening shifts pass. After a particularly trying night of fingers lingering where they shouldn't, I slip him my number, disgust clotting in my mouth.

Walking past the soaring arches of the Royal Courts of Justice, I think about what I will say to him, what he might say to me, and how every sentence of mine will best his.

*

On their wedding night, Ploy looked up at her husband. His pink, loose-skinned neck spoke painfully of human fragility. Her kind lived for centuries, her mother's blood running strong in her veins, her mother's voice sounding in her head, thick with shame and disappointment. *No daughter of mine would permit such indignities. Be rid of him; snap his spine.*

The bed creaked. Her husband grunted as he did when

struggling with a jar of marmalade. The slap of his body against hers was like sarcastic applause.

Afterwards, as she wiped herself, he asked her how it felt. Ploy looked at him through her eyelashes and murmured that she loved nothing better than to be taken like that, suppressing both laughter and revulsion as he studiously jotted down her words in a notepad.

She had acquiesced to marriage out of curiosity. Human heterosexuality seemed like a finger-trap puzzle that she could outsmart, and England sounded brighter than any realm she'd visited, a cold, perfect place glittering with rain and prestige. She found only spit-gobbed pavements, raw drizzle and poverty. She learned that this land, the birthplace of capitalism, was nourished by a strong belief that it was best for everyone to be slightly miserable, which made it impossible to acknowledge or alleviate its deep societal ills and pronounced lack of decent food.

One day, at the supermarket, Ploy picked up a plastic package of nine lychees, each small and tight as a house cat's balls. The price made her gasp. She bought them anyway.

That night, Steve took Ploy to a jazz club to see his favourite singer, his gaze flicking between his wife and the woman on stage. Chompoo had a brassy voice and a shirt front crisp as Riesling. Black silk stretched over her strong thighs and soft stomach; expressive hands grasped the microphone stand as they might the back of a lover's neck.

Ploy listened to the jazz singer, saw her painted lips, the fork at her trousers, her artful command of the audience. Eating dry, sour lychees from her handbag, she ran slick but kept her face straight. There was something otherworldly about the woman above her; she would have to investigate whether it was a performer's glamour or that she had finally found someone like herself.

To Steve's excitement, Ploy kept up a sullen silence until they got home.

'So, what did you think?' He flicked the hem of his notepad with a ragged thumbnail.

A little moue. 'She was alright, I suppose.' It was the right face, the right answer. He scribbled it down with glee.

*

Ploy asked for pain without a mark. Chompoo asked for complete silence, working her over with practised hands and a low, hard voice. It was the longest hour Ploy had ever known.

Afterwards, she borrowed a dressing gown and tottered to the bathroom, feeling with her tongue where she had bitten the inside of her cheek. She looked for traces of sex in the mirror but found only unbruised and lambent skin. When there was a knock at the door, she ducked out apologetically. A woman passed her quietly with a towel folded at her chest, tortoise-shell glasses slipping down her nose.

'You didn't tell me you had a roommate,' Ploy grinned when she returned to the bedroom. 'Is that why you wanted me to be quiet?'

Chompoo put down her tablet. 'I don't. Mot's escaping her husband. Like you, except out of fear and necessity, not contempt.'

The tart comment drew only a smirk from Ploy. 'Didn't have you down as the charitable type.'

'It isn't charity. It's helping each other because that's all we've got. Hating us is fundamental to the British state.'

'"Us"? Who's "us"? *We* aren't even people!'

Chompoo quirked an eyebrow. 'There's a difference between not being human and being dehumanised. You think Sharon at the Border Agency gives a shit that we're supernatural? We're all foreign.'

'Borders are bullshit. One trip over an interstitial threshold and you'd be spared this shithole. I could just hop over a trans-dimensional boundary like a skipping rope in a playground and disappear into a glorious space in between the walls of the world.'

'Oh, could you?' Chompoo laughed. 'My cousin was a musician at your mother's court. I hear the Queen curses your name to this day for taking your little sister, her favourite child, away from her. Such a scandal! I sympathise, you know, being the eldest daughter myself, though I'm just a lowly singer and you were a princess. We just want something of our own that's not the burden of expectation. But you paid such a high price ... is that why you're still here when it would be oh-so easy to leave, because of a sunken cost?'

Ploy pressed her lips together. It had been so long since she had met someone else from one of the heavenly realms, another being who understood things at a cosmological level, that she had forgotten her circumstances and let out an idle boast. How humiliating to be reminded of everything she had given up, her erstwhile status, her lost power of flight, how she had brought her baby sister down in the same way. That Chompoo could see through her bluster unnerved her, but it could be useful. She had never been challenged like this before. It made her want to scratch.

'Khontun like you always talk so much,' she said. 'Musicians are all mouth. It must make you feel good about yourself to take people in. I'm sure you enjoy playing the artiste with a heart of gold.'

Chompoo chuckled. 'Oh, I know I'm nobody. Those who are in between and out of place are my family. If I can help one other lost, lonely body, that's good enough.' She flashed a smile, earnest and lop-sided.

Ploy remembered the force of the wind at her wings, the power, the height. Bargaining away not just her gift but her sister's, too, was her life's only shame and regret. *If I can help one other lost, lonely body ...* She lingered on Chompoo's remark, considering matching it with the idea that fluttered in the back of her throat, but the only words she could muster were, 'I should go.'

A sigh. 'You're married to that farang.'

'He seemed gullible enough.'

'Have you ever thought about how your disdain, your surety of winning, is a privilege? You're right that borders are bullshit, but can you even begin to imagine what they mean for someone like Mot, how violent they are to anyone without an ounce of your power?'

Ploy moved her head from side to side, sensing an opening. 'You know, I was going to ask if you were interested in a proposition. Business and pleasure with a charitable heart. But if you find me so loathsome ...'

Chompoo spread her hands. 'No, I do like you. You're just—'

'You do? How sweet.' Ploy dressed quickly, lifting her hair out from inside her turtleneck. 'Are you going to ask Mother for my hand?'

'You talk too much, but go on.'

'I want to make a place for people like us. A sanctuary.'

*

Tonight is my first and last date, I hope. I am *THAI GIRL* again, smiling and smiling and smiling, a pretty wig curling about my face, a skirt around my hips. This candlelit pub in Bloomsbury would be pleasant if not for Steve sitting across from me, patiently explaining to me my thesis on challenging essentialised representations of refugees.

An Asian woman wipes down the next table, her glossy, slanted bob swinging with each movement. As I admire her bright green nails, something tugs at me, a feeling like pages rippling in the wind, and the name leaps out from my lips before I can calm myself.

'Ploy.' I watch Steve stop mid-sentence, his mouth slack as I continue. 'Tell me what happened to my sister.'

Steve starts to gabble: what a rotten trick, I can't possibly be Ploy's sister, and he has mostly forgotten about her, anyway. Then, his face changes. 'It was sudden,' he whispers. 'She came home one day and we ... argued.' His voice acquires a strange, soft quality, as if he is speaking through the skin of a dream. 'She wanted to leave. She wanted something only I could give, just one thing ...'

*

Steve often repeated that a man needed his own space, so Ploy felt an especial thrill from refusing to answer his calls.

He opened the door and found her swivelling gently in his office chair, paper in hand, legs high-crossed. She looked him in the eye and read his words back to him: descriptions of her dark eyes and capricious nature, her body's smell and capacity, the juvenile charms of her younger sister. The sheer size and clarity of her anger made her voice sound like a bell. 'You left this lying around. Did you think I couldn't read?'

'Darling, you're mistaken,' he explained slowly. 'These are notes for a novel. It's not real,' he smiled, 'it's art.'

'Perhaps I'm also mistaken about this memoir you've written about finding yourself in Thailand. *Third Wife Lucky*, you call it.'

'Well,' he said, 'I'm allowed to write a memoir. I don't need your permission.'

'Nor I yours. I'm leaving. Maybe I'll write a memoir about that.'

Her voice was so hard, so final, so mockingly different from the gentle, pliant woman he knew, that he understood all at once that everything had changed. His mouth formed a perfect O through which he took a dragging breath.

'How could you do this to me, after everything I've done for you?'

She smiled. 'Well, since you mention it, there's actually one last thing you can give me.' A boxcutter clicked in her hand.

*

'My memories of her,' says Steve. 'She must have taken them from my memoir. I know only that I was once married to a woman called Ploy and she left me. When I try to think of her face, our wedding day, it's like being jerked awake as you're falling asleep—you have to start all over again. So, you see, she hurt me too. She hurt both of us.'

He reaches for my hand, but I snap back and cuss him out until he flees, my seagull laughter chasing him out of the pub. The idea of running after him wielding my beer bottle is appealing, but my hands are shaking. I curl them in my lap and weep. I imagined this evening very differently, thinking that I'd triumphantly throw Steve aside like a curtain and Ploy would be there, but instead I'm no closer to finding her than I was as a schoolgirl flitting about the village.

It is soothing to press a paper napkin to my face, to puff into the firm pressure of my hands and the pink of my closed eyelids. No one bothers me. After a minute, I button my coat and leave.

Belisha beacons glow in the city grey. I sit under the bus shelter and watch nine pigeons delicately pick their way across the pavement. Somewhere behind me, a phone rings.

A light touch on my shoulder jolts me. 'It's for you.' It takes me a moment to place the barmaid, whose green nails shimmer as she offers me the handset, old and analogue, its cable coiling from somewhere above us. 'I think you've been waiting a long time.'

Nothing is making sense, but I am desperate for this. I scrabble at the smooth plastic, placing it against my ear.

My sister's voice—hers, fuzzy at the edges—is unmistakable.

'Ploy?' I breathe, a kite launching in my chest. 'Is that really you?'

She says my name, asks how I am as if casually picking up a conversation, as if she's been away for a handful of days and not hundreds.

My gaze meets the barmaid's gleaming cat-eyes. The pigeons turn as one and fly at my face in a clapping flurry, but instead of beaks, I feel only the softest feathers brushing my cheek.

The last thing I hear before falling headlong into shadow is the sound of my sister speaking. 'I'll see you very soon,' she whispers.

*

Ploy can feel her sister approaching along the passageway leading from the human world into the watery space between realms. The plan went off without a hitch. Soon her sister will be welcomed home to the Sanctuary in the old mall, where Ploy is busy arranging a room and a narrative for her.

Here is the story. High in the mountains where kinnaree bird-women fly to and fro between worlds, there once ruled a hard, unyielding queen. Her royal palace, stiff and ornamented, was not a worthy container for the desires that surged within her first daughter, who chafed at the idea of inheriting the throne and at her mother's indulgence of the youngest princess. Aching for more, Princess Ploy took her little sister and descended the mountainside into the Himmapan forest, home of the sages. There among the mushroom rings and mossy rocks, the two sisters met Lopamudra, a bright young rshika who dabbled in dark arts. They made an exchange with her, giving up their kinnaree wings to live instead as humans— humbly and peacefully, unencumbered by regal duty, each free to make her own meaning.

But it was nothing like Ploy expected, all this fleshy exist- ence and plodding about in the dust. She decided to abandon her life in the village and escaped with a farang for the excite- ment of England, leaving her little sister in the care of Auntie Somruay on the promise that it would just be for a little while.

The farang turned out to be more trouble than he was worth. A dear friend, Chompoo, helped Ploy out of her sticky situation, inspiring Ploy with her kindness. What if everybody had a sanc- tuary, she wondered. She set out again to find Lopamudra, now a full-fledged witch, to strike a second, more elaborate deal.

This time, Ploy asked for access to the Night Market in between planes of existence and to be granted a space to build her sanctuary in the abandoned mall. Most of all, she wanted to give her little sister a meaningful human life of adventure and discovery, which would peak with the marvellous revelation that she had been more than human all along.

The cost of the trade would be dear: Lopamudra demanded the obliteration of all records of Ploy's own human life, including her mnemonic existence in the lives of all who had known her. Only her little sister's memory loss would be impermanent, her recollections of Ploy held as a deposit until the ritual's conclusion, kept safe until they could be returned.

So, in the end, it would all be worth it.

*

The Night Market takes place on water that impeccably mirrors the sky, inconceivably black and swirled with perfect stars. Improbable structures emerge on its surface, criss-crossed by a lazy, endless parade of boats and ships of every imaginable form. Traders call out their wares, which can be neither item-ised nor quantified. I like best:

1. a non-binary auntie's impossible towers of dried fish, straps and sacred weapons, golden pikul flowers from the mouths of blessed yet beleaguered girls, and great loops of good fat sausages;
2. leaf-wrapped and stick-speared snacks sold by a leather daddy;
3. little dick-shaped charms laid out on blankets while Kuan Im, Nang Kwak and manekineko figurines cluster in corners and perch on ledges (business flows all around, and everyone wants a piece of their own luck).

My sister buys me a clutch of steamed toddy palm cakes, soft and yellow, the colour of happiness. 'Your favourite,' she beams. I crumble them into the water, feeding the lapping mouths, beaks and paired maxillae of fish and not-fish who dwell there. This is not out of spite: waking in a different realm with a head full of new memories unsettles the stomach, and I dislike wasting food. Undaunted, Ploy chatters brightly, barely letting questions fizzle out in the void of my sullenness before pursuing new topics.

I listen to the voices in the crowd. I'm surrounded by Thai, Isaan and Khorat, perhaps also Teochew, Tamil, Cham, Mon and what might be Pali. It could almost be home.

All at once, the beauty of everything turns into a roar. Faces and limbs seem to merge and blur into a trap all around me. Incense and jasmine wreaths mingling with cooked flesh, achingly familiar smoky-sweet smells, suddenly make me gag. I struggle away from the throng, wiping my face, feeling betrayed by my own body, and stumble forward until the heat of the crowd is behind me.

A boat steered by a handsomely dressed monkey draws my eye as it weaves between barges and stilt-legged stalls. I breathe slowly and stare at its rippling wake, noting the shifting patterns, and gradually the world resolves into something that does not cause me pain.

My ribs still hurt. I shift the bra wires uncomfortably encasing my torso. Among the first things I bought in the market were a series of sports bras and a binder, but Ploy tutted and took them from me, swapping them for some lacy Wacoal specimens before I could protest, telling me I needed to grow up. It rubs painfully against a memory of her long-ago embrace of my younger tom self. I wonder if England changed her.

I notice with a jolt that I've ended up in front of a small shopping mall. Its faded facade, hemmed with water stains and moss, crowned with dark, wispy, nameless flowers pushing out from cracks in the wall, makes my guts feel cold and heavy. I want to sink down into the mud with it. But it's not the shabbiness of the building that's prompting my dread—it's my sister.

'Ah, you've found your way home to the Sanctuary!' Ploy clasps her hands together, a picture of sororal delight, which then eloquently folds into concern. 'You shouldn't run off like that, you know. It makes me worry.'

The doors open smoothly onto a cool, quiet lobby. Glittering streams of water zigzag through the building in anticipation of boats and water-dwelling traders that never came. This place never took off as part of the main trade site, not because of a rejection of modernity per se—you'll find vibrators and vapes for sale in the markets—but more because something about the ley lines or glyphs around here isn't quite right for business.

At least, that's what Ploy tells me. She is talking to me again as we move through the quiet corridors.

'Little sister, what a delight it's been to welcome you home.' She inclines her head and after a brief pause continues as if my response had been encouraging. 'This abandoned mall has been *reclaimed* by women and sexual minorities as a *safe space*. All these units have been made into rooms where people can turn over their memories to us and start afresh. They get to *choose* if they come, they get to *choose* the memories they invest—it's just so empowering!'

My sister is interrupted by one of the safe space's guests. 'Ah, Mot, is it?' she says impatiently, looking down at the small woman bearing a clipboard, tortoise-shell glasses and an expression of deep exasperation. 'Can this wait? I'm catching up with my sister. Yes. Well. We really must be getting along ...'

Ploy steers me round a corner away from Mot.

'Where was I? Oh, yes, it was very important to us that this initiative be led by and for *women*. Now, I may be exiled mountain royalty while my partner is a ghandarva woman and our broker a transdimensional witch, but we are all *essentially* women, right?' The memory rubs again. 'And we gave up so much, especially me—us!—to make this place sustainable. A lot of rich memories and personal sacrifices. That's why we're able to help these people, little sister, and the vast majority of them appreciate us. You should feel proud.'

*

After I shut my bedroom door in my sister's face, the only sound is the smooth whirr of the ceiling fan. I ease myself onto the floor. I have no idea who Ploy is. Even though I can see what we share in feature and gesture and tone of voice, she is a stranger. How odd it is that she can dart effortlessly from businesswoman to attentive housekeeper to warm friend, I think, before catching myself. Isn't a woman allowed to be many things at once? I shake my head. No, the problem isn't that I lack the requisite feminism to understand that my sister is complicated. Her business arrangements obliterated chunks of my memory, all except for a carefully timed trail of crumbs that made sure I stayed in place until she was ready for me. Meanwhile, the resulting grief and confusion utterly obsessed my body, so that I am not even ready for myself.

I can't cope with the realisation that this longed-for reunion has pissed me off.

Ploy's voice comes through the door. It is breathier, wobbly at the edges. 'You were my favourite sister,' she begins, 'newly hatched, adorable. You followed me like a chick. Yes, you came with me down Mount Krailat, we swam together in the Bokkharani pond. We ate ripe mangoes the colour of sunset, remember?

'That evening, we returned not to our mountain palace but to a little human village. I wanted something unlike the fusty world of the heavenly court. Humans live short yet purposeful lives, and I thought we'd find it an amusing game.'

I do not remember any of this, which pleases me.

'Are you angry because I left you behind in Khorat?' she asks.

43

'I only did that because Steve told me to. Something about visas. We could bring you over later, he said, and I hated him for it, but I played along. I always provided for you—in human currency, and by making things easy for you, in my own way. Feeding you small dreams and little clues. It took a while to pull off the deal with Lopamudra, but we did it.'

After a pause, she continues. 'I haven't given much thought to how any of this weighs karmically, but I'm sure I'll pay for it, if that's any consolation ...'

I know she wants me to open the door and fall into her arms, eager for the warmth of sisterhood, grateful for renewed permission to dwell in the hollows and dells of my own memories. Instead, I swallow my tears and ask the question that has burned in my throat for hours, though I'm aware I'll never get the answer I need.

'You used me as money. Was your deal satisfactory?'

'Money.' She tastes the word for a moment. Then, her voice hardens. 'Well, on that topic, your postgraduate study, your new life in England—where do you think the funding and convenient arrangements came from? I did all of this for you, little sister. The least you could do is act grateful.'

There it is, laid out plainly. Our relationship is nothing but a series of transactions.

My fist against the door makes a satisfying noise. I hear her gasp and shuffle away.

*

Hours later, I tiptoe to the kitchen for a glass of water. Chompoo is there, making a huge bowl of Mama noodles, soaking them for far longer than usual. She smiles at me, quietly singing 'Minnie the Moocher' as she waits. I almost feel like smiling back. When the noodles are bloated to her liking, she offers me some.

Then I remember what I know about Chompoo and her complicity in Ploy's deal. I can't let my guard down, no matter how kind Chompoo is or how beautiful her voice. I turn smartly out of the kitchen and return to bed. As I leave, I hear the quiet clatter of utensils falling to the floor.

Mot is waiting for me around the corner. The corridors are dimly lit, casting everything in warm shadow. She stands by a huge potted plant with heart-shaped leaves that shade her like a tree, tilting back her head a little to regard me, her cheekbones deep-cut as the side of a mountain.

'You're right not to trust them.'

I don't know if I should trust her, either. Still, I might as well find out what I can. 'What did you want to talk to my sister for?' I enquire.

'Where to begin,' Mot groans. 'All the guests here have got something to say to management, but they never want to listen.' She presses her hands against the wall behind the potted plant, revealing a sliding door that seems to have appeared from thin air. 'We've been lied to, torn away from our communities and our own memories, left only with a void, a lack. You know what it's like. Someone comes up to you one day, they seem caring and a lot like you, and offers you sanctuary, promises that you'll never be hurt again by the enemy. By the time you know better, you can't leave—not in any meaningful way, not for anything better. Well, we've had enough.'

She opens the door a crack. Warmth and light and chatter spill out, threatening to make my ears ring again. 'Come in, there are some people I'd like you to meet.'

'Can't do crowds right now,' I stammer, shaking my head, not really expecting her to understand.

Mot simply nods and slips inside, returning a moment later with some blankets, a little tray of food, and a plastic bag filled with a bundle of fabric. My sports bras and binders. 'You bought them from my friend Alisa. She wanted to make sure you got them.'

I don't know what else to do but mumble my thanks and pick at the food. It's good—plain white rice and mince stir-fried with pounded turmeric, lemongrass and chilli. I'm not hungry, yet somehow my body is greedy for it.

The heat makes my eyes and nose run. Mot misunderstands me and offers me unnecessary kindness. I tell her I'm fine, but she keeps saying, 'It's all right. There's a lot to think about,' handing me tissue after tissue. I'm sick of women fussing over me when I don't know what they want in return, so I get up to leave.

'This is too much for you,' she says quietly, 'I get it. We're trying to solve the problem together. Come find us when you need us. We'll always be here for you.'

Anger inexplicably grips my throat. I feel words collecting at the base of my jaw from out of nowhere, the simmering urge to scream—about how we've been sucked in by the void, we're all just *nothings* talking about *nothing* with *nothing* coming of it. If the problem is the nothing, the hole where our memories were within us and where our bodies were in the fabric of our communities, what could ever fill that void? Nothing.

I say nothing and walk away.

*

Sex is fluid, Chompoo reflects, not just because of the messiness of a good fuck, but because of how power flows through fucking. She thinks of how she needs to be desired when she performs. To command the stage, she needs to drink the rapt attention of the audience; to command Ploy, she needs Ploy to need her to take her apart.

But something about the past few days has given fresh vigour to her worming doubts about whether Ploy really needs her at all. Chompoo thinks about how she has always been the listener, her girlfriend the sweet-talker, and of how the power she commands in the bedroom evaporates outside it. In all other aspects of their life together, she has never been able to say no to Ploy. Here again, she is pestered by that awful, wriggling idea that Ploy is only chucking her under the chin, humouring her and the seriousness of her wishes and desires. Usually, Chompoo can shove such thoughts between the sofa cushions and sit on top of them, but the return of Ploy's sibling has shaken her. It was meant to be a family coming back together, the anticipated end to a long separation, and once everyone was in their rightful place, they were supposed to continue ever onwards into hazy, light-filled bliss, all pink and gold and laughter. The terms of the deal would be fulfilled; everyone would finally be free.

But Ploy's sibling arrived in the Sanctuary with a thump, slamming the door behind them and upsetting everything. With the building wobbling around her, Chompoo suddenly realises how many confused, grieving, dissatisfied women and queers have already knocked down the walls of their angry little rooms, forming a big hall and filling it with their voices.

'Do you ever stop and think about what we're doing?' she asks Ploy one night.

Ploy smiles brightly, simply, like a child. Her hands move in little circles around her face, working a series of toners, serums and creams into its surface. 'We're having fun,' she says.

'No, I mean, how we're trying to help people.'

There is a pause. 'I knew what you meant the first time.' Ploy's voice is already hushed, dangerous. Chompoo goes on.

'It's not even just memories that we're taking, is it? It's whatever vulnerable people offer us, we're not fussed if what we take is connected to their personality, selfhood, growth, relationships, their ability to live daily life—'

'That's what makes memories so valuable, valuable enough for us to run the Sanctuary at all. You know, at other places, people are made to recite their traumas repeatedly to access help. We're different. Isn't it better that we take those memories away rather than forcing people to relive them again and again?'

'If we were really different, we wouldn't take anything from them. We'd just help people because they need it.'

Ploy sighs irritably. 'It doesn't work like that. Besides, you've never complained before.'

Chompoo thinks back to the conversation after they first went to bed together, the only time she has challenged Ploy. 'You know that's not true.'

'We can have a meeting about this tomorrow.'

Sensing that she is boring her, Chompoo says something purely to provoke. 'What about your ... your younger sibling? Do you even know what they think?'

Ploy gets into bed and angrily smooths a sheet mask over her face. 'She's my little sister and we're together as a family again. I hope you understand that's worth everything.'

It is only after Ploy unclenches into true, fathomless dreams that Chompoo is able to close her eyes.

＊

In old stories, you hear of forest hermits gifting helpful items to adventurers and boons delivered by deities. Inevitably, being removed from ordinary human society, these blessings make everything worse. Perhaps this is the fundamental difference between my sister and me: while she viewed human life as a diversion, mortal life is all I can remember.

I think about Mot and her gathering of guests. Where had my sudden anger come from? Why had Mot's kindness stung me beyond words? What about the collective repelled me? I can't answer. I feel bereft of language, as if I have no edges, as though I wouldn't be seen in a mirror. Or perhaps it's that Mot *could* see me, and that she recognised something in me that I resent without being able to explain why.

My mind turns to revenge and resources, things I can grasp more confidently, around which my language is strong, articulate, practised. I wonder what it's like to acquire and command materials, to set prices and have them paid. Someone must have facilitated Ploy's deal. If they will be frank with me about their work, I'll walk in with eyes open and learn from them what I can.

I used to think finding my sister would complete me, but only I can do that. Her real gift to me has been a new sense of clarity, and I will allow myself to be grateful for this.

And when I leave, I'll have a lucky charm of my own.

*

The young person is alone, wearing a mouth painted the deep colour of an unbroken mangosteen above a black cocoon coat. A ring glitters on the fifth finger of their left hand.

Bittersweet solvents hang in the air. The witch already knows what the client wants, and she knows it is not quite what they need. Lopamudra only administers care through pain; she feels it is more honest. Of course you desire something so badly it hurts, she says, I understand. This is who you are, all the complex muscles, thoughts, veins, dreams, nerves clenched in pure want. Yes, dig your fingers into that soft pillow, balance yourself on the end of someone's tongue until they unmake you in the way you crave, speaking you into another existence. I know how to make that happen.

What excites her most is when people desire to become someone like her.

'I want to be a knife,' says the client. 'I want to understand how the edge of myself can open up someone else.'

'And you will,' says Lopamudra. 'Shall we begin, younger sibling?'

*

REPRESENTASIAN
MYTHOLOGIES (2)

In conversations about racism, non-Black Asians often reveal a dangerous mixture of both fear and longing in our attitudes towards Black communities. Such animus can lead directly to the incarceration of Black people, and it must urgently be addressed if we're to agitate for collective freedom. Although they may not do so explicitly, ESEA appeals to be seen and defended by the carceral state animate and exploit this anti-Black fear by engaging racist notions of criminality and innocence; the meek and harmless Asian victim is defined against the violent Black criminal from whom they need protection. These narratives intensify when incidents of violence against Asians by Black people receive a lot of media attention, and community grief is quickly channelled into calls for more policing. If we want to build a truly anti-racist movement, not only is it vital to refuse to adopt these carceral approaches to harm—we need to go further and actively commit to dismantling the police and prison system. There can be no anti-racist coalition and solidarity without fighting against the criminalisation of Black people.

Among ESEA activists, anti-Black rancour is stoked further by a commonly held belief that what we need and lack are things that Black people already have: a coherent discourse, representation, funding provisions, visibility, a slice of the neoliberal pie. When we say that Asians are an 'invisible' minority or that anti-Asian racism is 'particularly' normalised, these ideas are encrusted with a clear resentment towards

Black people, even when we don't openly name them as the target of our bitterness. But the hypervisibility of Black people, the anti-Blackness according to which state violence is structured, the subjection of Black people to early death over centuries—these are not things to envy. It galls me to have to say this. Moreover, as Olúfémi O. Táíwò observes, it isn't quite true that a bigger share of the attention economy brings greater access to the material economy.[1] High cultural visibility does not equal resources. If it did, then, to put it crudely, Black people—including Afro-Asian communities—would have been liberated long ago.

Alongside these resentments, many non-Black Asians also harbour a secret, anxious wish for racial reconciliation between Black and Asian people (and we can't seem to stop bothering Black Asian people about it). We—including myself, at this very moment—try to distance ourselves from those other, racist Asians in the vaguest terms. We may even share 'Yellow Peril for Black Power!' slogans on social media, a revolutionary gesture referencing a legacy of Black–Asian solidarity, but without really being able to name moments, relationships or movements in this history. Don't get me wrong, I think coalition is the way forward. But, to paraphrase Bernice Johnson Reagon, coalition is not the home; it isn't where we should go to seek comfort and nurturing, but a space where we'll be challenged and will often have to give things up. We keep asking Black people for reassurance, the emotional balm of being seen and heard as companions in struggle, rather than, I don't know, listening, strategising, or just … not being racist weirdos.

Meanwhile, Black histories often become mere appendages to our conversations about Asian histories—struggles we think we probably ought to be aware of but that are ultimately separate from 'our own'. We fail to see how all these threads intertwine with each other and together make up the histories of enslavement, indenture, imperialism and racial capitalism itself. Our understanding of racialised labour in the nineteenth-century Caribbean is limited to Indian and Chinese coolies, their struggles pried apart from those of formerly enslaved Africans, whose fight for freedom still continued after legal abolition. Instead of neatly dividing unfree labour in the Caribbean into a Black 'before' and a Chinese 'after', we could see what Lisa Lowe terms 'the intimacies of four continents' and their links in a continuous history of colonial exploitation and expansion.[2] Consider Tao Leigh Goffe's tender yet unflinching investigation into her Afro-Chinese family histories in Jamaica and her relatives' migration to the UK in the Windrush generation. Hoping to shed light on 'the invisible circuitry of Black and Asian life' through colonialism, she traces trajectories that struggle free and slip into the gaps of colonial structures as much as they are violently constrained by them.[3]

Taking stock of our ignorance, you could argue that when non-Black Asians claim to be invisible, we're being incredibly dishonest. Really, it's *us* who are refusing to do the seeing.

*

Here's another route we could take to think through these relationships. Writing in Britain in the late 1980s, Jamaican-born cultural theorist Stuart Hall noted a shift was taking place away from the idea of the 'essential black subject' and towards a conception of Blackness as a political and cultural construct, something relational, contested and unfixed. While this meant leaving behind the fictions of both essentialism and homogeneity, Hall argues that the dissolution of the stable category of Blackness was also bringing with it a confrontation with the 'immense diversity and differentiation of the historical and cultural experience of black subjects'.[4] What would the collapse of sameness mean for Black solidarity? Acknowledging both the difficulty and the urgency of the task ahead, Hall stresses the need to develop a politics that works 'with and through' these complicated notions of difference.[5]

There is also, of course, the bald fact of material difference. Challenging Hall, anti-racist political thinker A. Sivanandan decried all this 'construction' and demanded that we pay more attention to the economic base of cultural politics.[6] Focusing on labour and wealth, Sivanandan often makes reference to Sir Ieuan Maddock's remark that 'electronics had replaced the brain as once steam had replaced muscle', describing how technological development had impoverished the Global South, disrupted our relationships with the land, and shifted people through space like pawns to fill the labour requirements of capital.[7]

This brings us back to the matter of what race actually is, a question on which African feminist activist and researcher Zandi Sherman provides a useful framework: race is a technology and infrastructure, organising bodies according to the logic of racial capital.[8] Sivanandan quotes from a Malaysian brochure that describes how the speed and manual dexterity of 'the oriental female' supposedly make her ideal for working in silicon chip factories for large multinational companies, even as this labour quickly shortens her working life.[9] Race arranges the bodies of factory workers into an assembly line of eyes and hands, compelling them to work until these parts wear out. The same processes also lead us to the construction of another racialised subject: the 'yellow woman'. Anne Cheng's book *Ornamentalism* explores Asiatic femininity through the yellow woman as a racial spectre, the fantasy of a beautiful object, described through visual vocabulary of shiny silk, porcelain, metal, glass, synthetics.[10] Race-making occurs not only when the body is rendered into productive parts, but also in the creation of images and surfaces. Think of how certain gleaming, beautiful garments immediately evoke the figure of the yellow woman as exotic and open for use. Just as she can become a robot, she can also be made into a doll.

Far from being discrete, disconnected or relevant only to certain racialised bodies, these histories chart the very creation of race itself as a global scheme to organise labour in service of capital. We can't understand the plight of the 'oriental girl' or 'yellow woman' in isolation; her existence is only possible as part of a larger racial hierarchy for exploiting entire populations and extracting from their lands. While we can learn about the particularities of Asian histories and labour struggles, we should always return to this broader structural context and see how racial histories interconnect, including the central role that international solidarity has played over centuries of anti-racist resistance.

*

I repeat the uncomfortable phrases 'oriental female' and 'yellow woman' to highlight the fact that racial nomenclature is tied to labour, and to emphasise that swapping in the terms 'Asian' or 'ESEA' would not heal the injury. Perhaps my engagement with these descriptions is upsetting or confusing, given that so much of ESEA activism targets people who use the wrong words to racialise us, or who engage in 'cultural appropriation' by wearing qipaos or kimonos or farmer hats. You may also be wondering why I have not spoken against 'harmful stereotypes', nor proposed 'reclaiming our stories' or 'more ESEA-owned organisations'. Before delving into these ideas, I think it's important first of all to ask what we ultimately hope to achieve. Could more or better representation really bring about those transformations?

I'm not saying it's wrong to be angered or hurt by racist language, images and ideas. Rather, I want us to go beyond this stance of aggrieved innocence and use our indignation to dig deeper. When we do, we find that the problems we want to address are material and sustained materially through capitalism and the legacy of colonialism. Pursuing representation alone won't deliver the changes or results that we're after, although we can certainly use cultural products to open conversations about these issues. It's understandable to want our time to shine, and there's nothing wrong with trying to, so long as we ground our work in opposing the structures that harm us all, from the bottom upwards. What good is a decolonised theatre or art gallery run by and showcasing the work of 'respectable' ESEAs if precarious migrant workers still sweep its floors?

Instead of taking aim at the structures that categorise labour in this way for exploitation, ESEA cultural activists seek 'positive representation' to remedy the grave injustice of being wrongly classified. An example is the running theme in Represent-Asian discourse of disgust at being treated as though we're sex workers and always available for erotic work. These assumptions are seen as stemming from a 'racist stereotype' that harms the ESEA community and needs to be challenged. We've got it the wrong way round: by rejecting the image of the Asian sex worker as offensive, abject and shameful, we are enacting harm ourselves by contributing to the stigma against sex workers in our communities, turning our backs on the very people who are most vulnerable to suffering as a result of the narratives we're annoyed to be caught up in. If it's difficult just to be taken for a sex worker in our society, shouldn't the target of our disgust be the carceral state that makes it so dangerous to actually be one?

To see how this endangerment plays out, let's return to *Ornamentalism*. In the chapter 'Borders and Embroidery', Cheng explores the nineteenth-century US legal affair popularly known at the time as the 'Case of the Twenty-Two Lewd Chinese Women'. It concerned a group of young Chinese women who were refused entry to the United States and detained on board their ship because they were assumed by California's immigration commissioner to be 'lewd and debauched women', that is, sex workers, since they were travelling alone without husbands or children. California state courts affirmed the commissioner's right to order the women's deportation on this basis in a trial that involved bringing the women before 'expert' white

American men to be examined for signs of licentiousness, their hairstyles and hems peered at in the courts, their sleeves inspected for extravagant width or hidden bright-yellow silks. The ruling was ultimately overturned in an appeal upheld in the 1875 U.S. Supreme Court case *Chy Lung v. Freeman* (not out of mercy for the women, but because state governments had to be prevented from taking federal matters like immigration policy into their own hands). Given the women's treatment before their release, it may be tempting to protest, 'They weren't actually sex workers! They had done nothing wrong!', but that misses the point. Appeals to loaded definitions of respectability and innocence tacitly accept the dehumanisation of people excluded by these terms. To this day, migrants and sex workers continue to be harmed by the same structures that confined those women to a ship a century and a half ago.

Some RepresentAsian activists claim to be interested in deconstructing racial stereotypes as a route to 'decolonisation'. Well, why don't we apply these same insights to taking apart images of the police as heroes and the state as saviour? In the 'Nordic model approach to prostitution', which criminalises 'buying sex', the state positions itself as rescuing sex workers from work that is inherently degrading and male clients who are inherently violent. In practice, this model seriously endangers sex workers, increasing their risk of experiencing client violence, eviction, homelessness, exploitation and destitution, as well as their exposure to state violence, including surveillance, police harassment, arrest and deportation.[11] Like all work, especially the most precarious, the real way to ensure safety for people who make their living from sex work is to agitate for better working conditions and the alleviation of poverty. The desperation of many ESEA activists not to be associated with sex workers stops them from connecting with groups doing just that, like Red Canary Song, SWARM and the English Collective of Prostitutes, who continue a long legacy of erotic labourers organising together and building safety networks without police. Why complain about bad representation when you could join the fight against state violence?

Now that we can see racism is more than a problem of bigoted language and negative stereotypes, that it can't be solved through positive representation, let's look at how these mistaken ideas play into the state's hands.

*

The main organising space for the current wave of ESEA activism has been social media, where things have a way of being flattened into a uniform register and tone, a smooth scroll, tap-tap-tap. As Tamara K. Nopper has observed, the hashtag #StopAsianHate is used by Asians online to document a huge range of grievances, from mispronunciation of names to experiences of violence, all of which commingle to form the general impression of a large wave of anti-Asian 'hate'.[12] Nopper explains that law enforcement agencies have a vested interest in racist incidents being logged, since these records can be used as evidence that more surveillance and policing are needed to protect against so-called hate crime. Confiding in our communities about the harm we experience could be a way for us to help each other heal, pool knowledge and come up with strategies for liberation. Instead, we are more often collecting data for the state to feed directly into hate crime infrastructure.

The notion of hate crime, in which certain 'hateful' acts are declared criminal, is part of the state's model to redefine racism as individual instances of racially motivated prejudice, deflecting our attention away from the reality of racism as a structure built to organise, divide and control racialised labour. As Naomi Murakawa observes, with the promise that the state will protect us from racism by throwing people who are racist to us in jail, hate crime legislation is a way of welcoming Asians into the fold of the nation.[13] It's ironic that ESEA activists claim to oppose the idea of being an 'assimilated' model minority while at the same time happily agreeing to provide a steady flow of information about their lives to the state so that it will incarcerate people for their sake. It's clear that their issue with the model minority myth doesn't come from a desire to resist adapting to the state's demands; on the contrary, it's because they believe Asians need greater access to the state's carceral protection. Some ESEA activists may vaguely pay lip service to the idea that the model minority pits Asians against other racialised groups, yet in accepting the state's hate crime narrative, they don't consider their own role in strengthening a system that brings many people in these groups, often Black people, closer to imprisonment and death.

I shall pause here to note that both Nopper and Murakawa are Asian American, yet their insights are not irrelevant for people outside the US, racial capitalism and imperialism being structures that operate globally and must be resisted in kind. Their arguments can be read alongside work by organisers like Remember & Resist, a collective that aims to engage in abolitionist praxis within ESEA communities in the UK. R&R has also written critically about hate crime narratives, showing how, instead of keeping us safe, this framework allows the state to act as a protector while obscuring its own racism and even provides a pretext to integrate police into communities that may themselves be vulnerable to police violence, such as undocumented people.[14] We can see that authoritarian control over racialised groups is not limited to one country but extends the world over. Continuities can also be traced through history, as in the connections highlighted by Jun Pang between British colonial forces' violent crackdown on resistance in Hong Kong in 1966 and police repression of protests on British soil in the present day.[15]

Despite how harmful it is, countless ESEA groups in the UK have bought into the practice of hate crime reporting as a means of fighting racism against Asians. In February 2022, a consortium of fourteen ESEA organisations accepted funding from the state to develop a third-party hate crime reporting service, whose key deliverables include escalation of incidents to police and data-sharing agreements with police.[16] Assimilation doesn't just mean blending into a society by adopting its language, cuisine, religion or culture. It can also be a willingness to assist the state in its project of punishment and control. If the racialised body is one that works and works and works, then it can also be called on to act as the state's eyes, constantly surveilling others and never turning this scrutinising gaze back on the state itself. Despite its well-intentioned origins, ESEA discourse is creating precisely these subjects, encouraging people to assimilate as factory parts that carry out the carceral state's functions—the working machinery of imperialist modernity.

*

If we want to build a new world together from the ground upwards, we have to attend to the hopes, dreams and fundamental needs of our communities. How can we meet each other where we are, some of us starry-eyed for positive representation and more effective authoritarianism, while trying to nurture a different vision of the future?

First, we must insist on a strong counter-narrative and present alternatives. In place of RepresentAsian history and its bland offerings of civic pride, traumatic sacrifice and 'good' vs 'bad', we will have libraries that build our knowledge and critical understanding about radical histories of anti-racist struggle connecting people within and across communities. If we're asked how to improve the police, we will muster the courage and imagination it takes to say, *no police at all*. And however many translations are made of 'hate crime' information sheets, however many 'community consultations' take place with pro-police organisations, we will continue to match them with bystander intervention trainings and anti-raids workshops grounded in solidarity against state violence. We keep each other safe, strong and sharp with whatever tools we have, from whatever position we occupy. We already have everything we need to care for each other, even though it might not feel like it.

While we try to push for change, we must work with what we have. Sometimes, our ability to create safe spaces and trusting relationships is restricted by safeguarding policies and mandatory reporting duties that embed surveillance and policing in our work. To avoid this, we often find ourselves working against institutions from within and without, a difficult struggle that can lead us to burn out. We have to support each other in our collective resistance and carefully consider whether or not to work with people, organisations and spaces that will be hostile to our commitments. Our choices may be constrained, but we can't let this push us towards making nice with the state or compromising our ambition. In fact, it becomes even more urgent to hone a sharper edge to our vision, driving it more deeply into the struggles on the ground so we can see, in unrelenting light, the long roots of oppressive structures. Our healing requires insurgent politics.

It might also mean completely undoing ourselves. When the label 'ESEA' is offered to designate us as a group targeted by 'hate crime' and worthy of protection by the carceral system, do we want to organise under this term? Instead of assimilating with the state's project of control, how could we fit into the wider anti-racist movement against state violence? Sometimes we might have reasons to be 'ESEA', or to abandon it, or to come back to it again. Political and racial categories are never fixed, and we should question attempts to make them stable. The point is not to maintain any formation for its own sake; it is to do the work of abolition. We make ourselves in order to destroy ourselves, becoming compost for the next thing.

We should not think that representation politics has already succeeded. It is seductive, yes, but it hasn't completely encased our future behind its glassy surface. We can—and must—carry on dreaming bigger.

*

SKIN LIKE SUNLIGHT
THROUGH WATER

Nipah has the same dream every night. She finds herself wandering around an iteration of her empty childhood home, over and under its stilt legs, through its warm, shadowy rooms. She has dreamed like this for almost twenty years. It's part of the rhythm of life, like getting groceries, sending money each month, and the ginger-and-lemon tea she takes every morning.

In the waking world, she is warming her hands around her steaming mug, trying to plan the day ahead while still stuck in a dream. By now, the architecture of her old house has shifted into a more ornate ruean thai, but there are still infinite rooms and, strangely, the occasional intrusion of what looks like an abandoned shopping mall. Worse, she increasingly encounters a handsome young man who eyes her suspiciously. It's been years since she concerned herself with what young men think of her, and the reminder rankles. Whenever she sees him, she knows the dream is about to end abruptly.

The boiler grumbles and yawns. Nipah sips her bracingly sour tea and makes herself get on with the morning. Every day, no matter what, she makes her daughter a hot breakfast, even if it's only fried eggs with maggi on rice.

*

If you've ever met an auntie whose forbidding bone structure and brusque demeanour made you feel like a scolded child, you have met Nipah. Her perfect posture, voluminous black hair and lack of indoor voice means that she seems much more imposing than the 151 centimetres allotted to her by nature. Nipah has every right to be a proud woman. She likes to remind herself that she is well-educated; she brought herself from Nonthaburi to England and brought forth a daughter from her body, a child who not only grew a little taller than her but also speaks perfect English-from-England and goes to university. Her name is Thames.

Nipah was a little upset, she admits, when her daughter said she wanted to go to university in Birmingham—if she was going to leave London, then it would be for Oxbridge—but that's only because she loves her so much.

'You're my heart,' Nipah likes to say, usually after causing a fuss that has made her daughter stare numbly into space.

In the end, Thames went to SOAS. It's not ideal, since it's the place that prompted Fah-sai's decline, but no other London uni wanted her, and at least it's close to home.

*

crushedlittlestars:
so are you and your mum good now
like
what were you fighting about this time
was she mad that you wanted to see fah-sai again?

srirachini69:
Omg June, why are you so obsessed with me and my mum?
Also yes

crushedlittlestars:
babe you know this isnt normal right
like im glad you ended up at SOAS with me but you didnt rly have a choice...u should have been able to go anywhere you wanted you need to set boundaries

srirachini69:

?

Boundaries sounds like a white people thing. Leave me alone [cry-laugh]

crushedlittlestars:

ok thames

firstly i need you to stop invalidating my identity, i have picked the winning team (asian), secondly i know you love [potato] [potato] [potato]

but seriously. u cant still be thinking of going to thailand w your mum for 4 weeks??

srirachini69:

It will be the first time in ages. You know how anxious she gets about revocation. She won't go without me, I don't have anyone I can stay with that she trusts.

crushedlittlestars:

ok so maybe your mum isn't being super paranoid about the citizenship thing but uhh she could campaign for migrant rights and not control her daughter's every move

also [face with monocle] YOU ARE 20 YEARS OLD

couldnt u try to meet fah-sai on your own? isn't she friends w namfon and her mum?

srirachini69:

Haha ok... you're telling me everything with your mum is all hunky dory whenever you want to do something?

Also yes I could technically meet up with her but it would really upset my mum, so yeah [long-haired person shrugging]

crushedlittlestars:

lol no but she also doesn't scream at me or snoop through my

messages. she understands we are separate people.
like. physically.

srirachini69:
??? It's so rude of you to talk about my mum like that, especially when she likes you. In fact if you weren't in York she would've let me stay with you.

So if you really think about it... this is all YOUR fault. :)

crushedlittlestars:
wow. ok then

*

Revocation is a fear that gnaws at Nipah night and day. The possibility of losing her British citizenship in her mind has to do with racism, disrespect for the monarchy, Brexit and communism. At least, those are the most popular topics in the Line chats with her friends from the temple. The country is losing its way! Nobody is safe anymore! People are destroying our way of life! Thailand and Britain swirl into one nation, endangered from within and without.

When Nipah first came to England, she quickly understood the lay of the land. She learned from well-educated Thai people like her about the need to categorically distinguish herself from other migrants from other places. Being Thai is unthreatening and just right for England: proper Thainess, just like proper Englishness, requires a polite and hardworking body. This was instilled in Nipah from childhood through fist, word and image, through books with children who wore clothes on the top and bottom parts of their bodies at all times, girls long-haired in skirts, boys short-haired in trousers. In the old days, children would play mostly naked while men and women, all short-haired in loincloths, exposed their torsos to the sun. Modernity meant clothing, because nakedness is unsightly. You mustn't bare your skin and run wild but should cover it in crisp, white cotton so you can go to work or school, standing starch-stiff as the red, white and blue flag is hoisted above you. That is what distinguishes a village brat from a citizen.

Nipah finds it comforting that you can understand yourself through constant comparison to other people. How else would you know your place in the world? Whoever you are, at least you know you're not like *those* people, at least you're not like *that*.

A handful of flesh does not lie. Its truth can be read by other people, and the truth hurts. Nipah prepares Thames for the sting of rejection. In Thailand, people will not hesitate to tell her she is fat; they will point at her scars and stretchmarks. Thames doesn't understand and says farang do this too. No, Nipah tries to explain—like everything else, it's *different* when Thai people do it. You know what Thai people are like, she says, buying a holiday swimsuit that will cover Thames from chin to heel.

The greatest gift her daughter has is the knowledge that she is not beautiful. Nipah has seen how vanity and boyfriends make young girls lose themselves. Thames is untouched by all this—except for that one stupid misunderstanding, which was over quickly, thankfully.

*

'Get me one of the things that you can throw at people's heads,' says Nipah. Thames chuckles–only Mum would describe little cooking pumpkins like this. She brings one home for her mother from Chinatown, cradling its dark curve. Nipah delicately traces the point of a knife through the skin before attacking it with a cleaver, bright orange splitting green with a crack. The squash is thwacked into pieces and garlic is ruth-lessly minced.

In a CorningWare casserole on the stove, some plain soup

already simmers away—what white people have taken to calling a 'bone broth', made with old and new bones boiled and re-boiled countless times, like family resentments. Nipah gets out a great wok with a black rainbow belly and sets it on the fiercest burner. She slices a tube of egg tofu into fat buttery discs and fries them till their outsides are blistered gold and their insides molten. They are set aside as she sees to the squash, orange woody flesh yielding to oil, steam and garlic. A teaspoon of yellow bean sauce kept in a peanut butter jar. Two eggs cracked one-handed, almost allowed to set before being quickly scrambled. On the table: pumpkin-and-egg stir fry; the casserole of soup with glass noodles, lily flowers, wood ears, watercress, fried tofu; remnants of a spicy tinned sardine salad; a dipping dish with fish sauce and sliced chilli; special organic 'Husband-Forgetting' heirloom rice, so named because it's so delicious it'll make you abandon your spouse. Forks and spoons are laid, and her daughter is called.

Nothing could be better than this, Thames thinks. She knows that Nipah will fuss over her body later, but it's worth it. She's seen those posts on how cut fruit is a love language. It's just how things are.

*

Nipah is standing in a mall in Bangkok, and the young man from her dreams is walking towards her. It's him—of that she is sure.

She squeezes Thames' hand. After a moment of puzzlement, the squeeze is returned. Thames thinks her mum is probably just excited. Nipah wants to make sure she isn't dreaming.

Namfon approaches them slowly, hunched over, her hands in her pockets. This is the first time Auntie Nipah has seen her like this, and Auntie can be a little ... well.

Nipah notices her daughter mirroring her own shock as she looks at Namfon. For a second, she thinks Thames is also processing the disconcertion of finding a dream come unstuck in real life, but then she shakes herself. She can feel her face practising the correct expression and again squeezes her daughter's hand, this time maintaining the pressure until Thames also rearranges her features.

Round and dressed in bright colours, a woman who only reaches Namfon's shoulder pulls Nipah into a warm embrace. Nipah smiles kindly at her friend, Namfon's mother, Pannee.

As they go through all the *wai*-ing and *how-are-you* and *how-was-the-journey* and *let's-eat-I-know-a-place*, Nipah's excitement merges with dread and confusion. How could Namfon have turned out like *that*? She feels briefly superior to Pannee, and this makes her feel better, but for a twinge of guilt. She has known Pannee since they were both gap-toothed children at netnari. Pannee has always been so kind, but also a little odd and probably, sadly, a red shirt. They never talk about things like this, they never had to—but recently, just under the skin of her friend's words, there has been something new that escapes Nipah's understanding, and it frightens her. She wants just one day without feeling like she could lose everything at any second.

*

The joy or failure of suki is the revelation of tastes and personality flaws, which are dipped, blanched and beaten into the hotpot. The meal comprises ingredients cooked too thoroughly (over-caution, inattention) or not enough (rashness, impatience). It's novel—in England they eat mostly fork-and-spoon meals—and Pannee provides a running commentary that makes Nipah snort. Nipah, in turn, gives Pannee the fattest prawns, a shared favourite.

Namfon senses that something has changed in Thames. There has been a distance between them ever since Namfon embraced her tom identity, cutting her hair short and learning how to take care of girls. She's a little worried that Nipah might have been trying to turn Thames away from her, as she has been doing with Fah-sai. She hopes she can draw her friend back out on her own terms.

'So, are you studying?' she asks. 'Working?'

It takes Thames a moment to answer Namfon's question. Those long-fingered hands, the soft line where warm skin turns palm-pink, so like her own …

'Second-year archaeology. I tutor English some weekends. You?'

'Really? Me too—well, I volunteer at an after-school coding club for pathom girls. Linguistics is my field.'

Thames can't pinpoint exactly when she realised her feelings. Namfon was always only a vague presence, someone over there in Thailand, until one day she cut her hair and started posting photos that showed off the back of her neck. Thames makes a note to go back through Namfon's posts, to scroll right down to the very first photo on her grid. But it will never be enough.

Namfon notices that Thames' eyes often worriedly flick towards Nipah. She offers Thames a slice of pork belly, juicy and well-marbled.

Thames gasps. 'Oh, my favourite!'

'I know,' Namfon smiles. 'I saw the story you posted about wanting some.'

Shame pulse gently in Thames' ears. The fact that her crush can perceive her too is outrageous. Her body doesn't feel like her own; she is a vessel of pixels being conveyed towards Namfon by forces bigger than herself.

Nipah and Pannee fight good-naturedly over the bill, snatching and screaming until Pannee narrowly wins. Thames relaxes a little. Her mother hasn't laughed this much in ages, her peals of joy swelling and breaking like a sob.

It's almost a relief to have a crush, Thames realises, as she and Nipah make their way back to the hotel. Wanting things is awful, but at least it gives her something to think about that isn't revocation or vigilance or constant guilt.

*

srirachini69:
Omg what do I do she's so hot
HELLO I AM HAVING A CRISIS
CAN YOU STOP PLEASURING YOUR NUMEROUS LOVERS
AND ATTEND TO ME,
YOUR BEST FRIEND

crushedlittlestars:
can u chill the fuck out pls? we are on different sides of the
world!!!!!
pls clarify for me. are u related to your crush...?

srirachini69:
Noo, her mum isn't really my auntie. Every woman older than
your mum is an auntie. Why are you asking, I thought you had
picked the winning team (Asian)?

crushedlittlestars:
stfu i knew that second part but am glad u clarified the first part
because PHEW
so theyre just a childhood friend who has become extremely
hot
and not like an actual cousin
ok good it's safe for you to be like this
[image of a comedic tableau: a girl dramatically posing over a
small waterfall so that it seems to gush powerfully from between
her legs; she is supported by her friends]

*

Nipah has apologised to Thames for giving her the following

things: ugly armpits, thick legs, skin easily stretch-marked and scarred.

She loves caring for her daughter. A while ago, she started a little skincare routine. It took some persuading, but Thames now lies silently facedown every night while Nipah polishes her skin with pink oil and a bumpy plastic implement, working it into the backs of those big calves, so like hers, creeping up the ticklish inner knees and thighs, scars hashing the skin near the hip and down one arm. Nipah can't pretend to comprehend how this—how *it*— happened. She fussed when she first found out about *it*, but that was only because she cared. She asked Thames repeatedly why she did *it*—what on earth could be so terrible, with their comfortable home and clean tap water and free education, as to turn her against her own body? What could make her act so abnormally, make her behave like one of *those* people? Thames' response to her mother's questions was to sit sullen and tight-lipped or speak back uncivilly, so Nipah was forced to conclude that she must have learned *it* from the internet or one of her friends.

In fact, she knows that Fah-sai, the child of a temple friend, had something to do with it. Nipah once adored how Fah-sai acted as an older sister to Thames, which made her betrayal even worse. When the inevitable discontents of adolescence come, instead of maturely accepting that all life is suffering, people like Fah-sai start falling in with the wrong crowd at university and doing upsetting things, like getting tattoos, denouncing the British *and* Thai states, becoming trade unionists—and not the old respectable ones, radical ones led by *those* kinds of people, like cleaners and prostitutes—and then they decide to go to Chiang Mai to talk to even more of *those* kinds of people, transsexuals and prostitutes and transsexual prostitutes, because, well, Nipah doesn't understand why, Fah-sai just seemed to think it was important, and then she never came back to England. It twists her guts terribly to think that Thames might be going down the same road.

Fah-sai has never said so, but Nipah knows, in the same

way that she knows Fah-sai put ideas into her daughter's head, that the reason she hasn't returned is that *her citizenship was revoked!* Why, it can happen to anyone if they aren't careful. Citizenship is removed when the home secretary believes it to be conducive to the public good, as with people who are terrorists and troublemakers. There are other ways to lose your right to be here, too. Didn't a whole generation of British citizens come here from the Caribbean to labour at the behest of the British state, only for that same state, decades later, to disown them and their children and grandchildren? Now, maybe some people think this is all a combination of organised neglect and violent targeting of specific groups according to the structures and legacies of colonialism, but Nipah knows better. The truth is, you simply have to avoid being like *that*, like *those* people. After all, there are some things you can't expect the state to tolerate. The nation has a right to demand things of its citizens.

She wishes she could make Thames understand how frightening it is to have a sick daughter. The GP said that counselling was the best option. Before their first session, Nipah approached Thames (who was finally eating again, albeit at odd hours and only in very small amounts) to tell her she was free to say whatever she wanted to the counsellors, she knew she was a good parent because she had sacrificed everything, and remember, if she wanted to, she could always leave Thames in London and go back to Thailand.

Thames was discharged soon afterwards. She had refused to speak during the sessions.

The important thing is that Thames stopped doing *it* and seems to be alright these days, mostly. Slowly, Nipah allowed Thames to see her friends again. Now she asks to see Thames' messages only sometimes—not always, not anymore. But the fear has never completely gone away.

*

srirachini69:
Hey Fah-sai! I don't know if you remember me but we were friends from Wat Thai. I'm in Bangkok right now, if you're around we could meet up? I'm here until the end of the month. I really miss you.
Sorry if that's inappropriate.
There's things you understand better than anyone and I wish you were here.
I could have started talking to you sooner, but my mum... well, same old mum. But I'm trying to be braver now.
Sorry. This is all a bit much.
I'm so sorry.

*

After the hotpot, back at the hotel, Nipah polishes Thames' skin with extra vigour.

Thames focuses carefully, pushing away the obscene skin-slick noises, *shlp-shlp-shlp*, so that she can form the sentence that might get her what she wants. 'Mum,' she begins, before correcting herself. 'Mother. Namfon asked if I wanted to go swimming with her tomorrow at the samosorn.'

It comes out in a rush, yet each word has been carefully considered. Thames' evident caution, as if she were approaching an unexpected and very large gecko in the bathroom, prompts anger to rise in Nipah's throat. Determined to show she's a reasonable parent, she swallows her irritation down, along with her worries about her daughter's company. After all, Namfon is the child of her oldest and most beloved friend and, despite her appearance, has always behaved responsibly.

'Be back for dinner at eight,' she says.

*

(Nipah dreams, jetlagged. Somehow, she knows this dream is tethered to another person's gaze, that she has closed her eyes to sleep and opened them on someone else's life.)

This is how you enter a house that doesn't quite exist. First, unbolt the gate, then, uncover the rain jar on the front porch. As the phone in your hand moves over the opening, there's always that lurch in your gut, the certainty that it will fall and be lost, and how terrible that would be, you're unusually attached to this ancient, slow, cracked thing … The device is caught mid-air, and by the time you realise it's alright, you're inside.

(She knows this isn't her dream anymore, but Nipah stays and watches the young man, her friend's daughter. What else can she do? It's so beautiful here, in this strange house …)

Each night, an app on your phone gently pulls you along a silver thread into someone else's dreams. Often, they are dreams that have stayed the same for years, which have a stability to their structure. You don't know whose dreams they are, if the dreamers know their sleeping stories have become this stuff stored in phones, if it bothers them that their secret worlds are being used as material for you to assemble your own.

This dream, the ruean thai dream, is in a place of pale green light and smooth wood, a house that welcomes water, which pools in rooms and gushes over balconies, silver in movement and black in stillness. There are carp and ung-ang, the latter gathered in a semi-circle, amphibian piphat singing from a classical repertoire.

The people you love are here with you tonight—Ladda and Fah-sai, Note and Caramel—splashing about and laughing. This is only the second time that you've all managed to share a dream.

Before the ruean thai dream, there was the golf course dream, the nail salon dream, the mathayom dream. A curious thing is that every dreamworld you inhabit blurs, superimposing itself on the same structure, always somewhere over there in the distance.

Whenever you find that juncture, that not-border, you cautiously explore more. Tonight, you've made it as far as the vestibule with the broken-up Kinokuniya. You think it's an abandoned shopping mall that exists in another plane just to the side of yours, beyond the ruins of capitalism, a place where the sharp blades of borders are turned into dreamstuff ...

(Once, Namfon was an innocent child, happily running about,
a whole future ahead of her. How did she turn out like this,
like *those* people? How did Namfon arrive at herself?
Who is inside whom? The idea of being invaded
makes Nipah sick with fury.)

There's that queasy anger—the intrusion, the feeling of being watched is back ... something thin and permeating, cold oil poured on your spine and soaking into you, sinking—
    The phone rings, and you are called back outside.

*

crushedlittlestars:
ok so -
you dont need to call it 'abuse' if u dont want. but you dont even like
allow yourself
to call it harm. to even think of it as hurtful.

srirachini69:
You don't get it. I've heard what her childhood was like, that's actual harm. Constant beatings. Destroying her stuff. The stuff she does to me is just off-putting and weird, she's just trying to show she cares about me. She's from a different time and a different culture.

crushedlittlestars:
ok. you did me this kindness when i was making the same excuses for my stepbrother and my exes, so -
the mum who always finds a reason to scream at you in front of her friends is the same mum who has always cooked you hot breakfasts.
the mum who laughed at you when you said an older yt boy from school wanted you as his thai bride, the mum who held you down on the bed to examine you when you said he touched you, is the same mum who knits you perfect jumpers and gives great hugs.
the mum who is never wrong because she is always scared is the same mum who tells you she loves you every day.
you are really jumpy
5 seconds of heated conversation make you start crying and shaking

srirachini69:
June, that's just because I'm weak. If I was a better daughter I could handle it.
Still gonna hold my mum's hand that she uses to hurt me because I can feel how small she really is.

*

Namfon climbs on her bike and gestures for Thames to join her. Thames hesitates, wondering if a fat joke is just around the corner. Namfon simply waits until she gets on.

They arrive at the samosorn, which is worn but well-kept. Thames emerges from the changing rooms wearing the same full-coverage swimsuit as Namfon, who chuckles and takes a running jump into the bright, blue pool. Her hair is otter-sleek when she resurfaces. 'Come on.'

It takes Thames several minutes to gather her mass of hair and stuff it into her cap.

They float in the water, chlorine and sunshine, limbs star-fishing, eyes dreaming. More than once, perhaps by accident, their hands touch.

Afterwards, Namfon accepts durian-and-coconut ice cream as thanks, wielding her spoon like a spade. She watches as Thames twists her hair off her neck, its length spilling over one shoulder.

'I know that look,' she says. 'You want it gone.'

Thames' first thought is, *what would my mother think?*

Namfon continues. 'My barber could probably fit you in after lunch. It'd be my treat.'

Thames' second thought is, *it's my body, isn't it?*

'Do you want to, or ...?'

'Yes,' says Thames. 'Let's do it.'

*

'You can't mean that, Nipah.' Pannee frowns. 'I understand you don't get along with Fah-sai, but she and Thames were friends for so long, and I just thought it would be nice to go up and see her in Chiang Mai now that you're all in the same country.'

Nipah wonders how on earth she ended up like this, sipping coffee with Pannee feeling as though she is slipping beyond her friend's grasp. 'No. Never again. I will never allow Thames to see Fah-sai ever again,' she repeats. 'You know what she did.'

'But that's my point. She hasn't actually done anything.' Ordinarily, Pannee tries to soften her language with Nipah, with whom disagreement requires the strategic arrangement of words harkening back to earlier days, folded around polite yet direct persuasion. This time, though, she's fed up. 'I'm trying to get you to understand that Fah-sai is a young woman who made choices that you wouldn't, but she still thinks of you and wants to see you.'

Nipah's hand trembles against the glass table. 'You can't know what it's like to find your daughter's shirts stained with blood. Fah-sai hurt us very much. We do not need this sort of disruption.'

She nobly forbears to say that her friends from the Wimbledon temple would understand. Pannee could afford to be soft on her child because she was surrounded by Thainess, but Nipah had to make her culture hard and strong, lest everything went farang. She wishes Pannee could see that. How did so much change between them?

Pannee sighs. She hates seeing this side of Nipah. Though she feels she has failed Thames and Fah-sai, years of friendship have taught her that argument never wears Nipah down but only invigorates her.

'Shall we get dressed for dinner?' she asks, accepting defeat.

*

crushedlittlestars:
hope things w ur crush are....... progressing *[winking face]* *[aubergine]* *[sweat drops]*

*

Namfon's barber's is in fact someone's house. Thames rolls back a greenish-blue gate and steps into a courtyard scattered with piles of spare parts, lush potted plants, washing tubs, big urns with little fish ponds inside them, baskets, tins and exhausted-looking sandals.

A fat, smiling girl in a floaty dress stands on the porch, her back to the giant computer rig just inside the front room of the house. She is gallingly beautiful.

'This is my girlfriend, Ladda,' says Namfon.

Thames smiles back even though she feels like the inside of her neck is being scraped out.

'Thames, right?' says the girl. 'Such a cute name. Thames and Namfon, a river and the rain, the things that England and

Thailand share. How gorgeous.'

'You shit!' Namfon is suddenly accosted by a short, stocky charmer with a topknot. 'You never return my fucking—oh, hello.' Caramel breaks into a grin when they notice Thames. 'Who's this, then?'

Moments later, Thames is sitting on one of the many little stools in the courtyard swaddled in a hairdressing cape. Caramel gathers her hair at the nape to feed it through the gown, while Ladda gently retrieves her hands from somewhere inside the fabric.

'Now, beautiful, show us what you want,' says Ladda, handing Thames a tablet computer.

Thames starts sweating, inchoate images swimming in her mind. What are the words that will point to what she wants? *'hot enbies mood board'*? *'transmasc haircuts that don't involve tiny fringes'*?

'I don't want to be beautiful. I want to be handsome.' It comes out more sharply than Thames intended, but this only rouses murmurs of delight from her new friends.

Ladda reaches over Thames' shoulder and taps a few words into the search engine. Somehow, right there on the screen before her is the very thing that Thames wants. Caramel grunts approvingly.

Thames' hair comes off in two easy swipes. Then comes a complex exercise of trimming and cutting and spraying and buzzing. For all their sweary gruffness, Caramel uses their hands with tenderness unlike anything Thames has known, describing every step of the process and always asking her permission.

'Thank you for doing this,' Thames says.

Ladda has brought out a huge laptop and settled in Namfon's lap on the porch. 'Yeah, Caramel is really good,' she says. 'Note doesn't trust anyone else for their haircuts.'

'Note?'

'Yes, a friend from the year below me. Fah-sai introduced us, actually. Might meet them later. I hope they bring dinner from that Isan place down the road.'

'Ah, me and Thames are going out with our mums this evening,' says Namfon, swiftly casting an eye over Thames' frozen smile.

'You won't stay?'

Namfon says nothing and squeezes Ladda, who smiles radiantly, which makes Thames want to run screaming down the road. She pinches herself a little underneath the hairdressing cape instead.

When Caramel softly brushes the last stray hairs off Thames' face and holds a mirror before her, she comes undone. She sees how Ladda and Namfon look perfect together, how Caramel has so gently yet thoroughly transformed her, how there is something of Namfon in her, too—she too can be a beautiful boy and a handsome girl, and maybe hot enbies and transmascs with tiny fringes will find beauty in her, too ... but would a handsome girl look away from her beautiful transfemme girlfriend and turn towards her?

The possibility of being looked at and desired, of something that isn't longing or jealousy, is overwhelming. She thought that getting a haircut would make things fit, would get the edges of everything to stick down. She hadn't considered that it would make all her feelings even bigger to the point where they'd be bursting free. How could she be so stupid? What you want always leaks out of you in the end.

And then, Namfon is there. 'Thames. Drink this water.'

'It's never just a haircut,' Caramel says. 'Never just clothes. Not for us.'

'You were very brave to tell us what you wanted.' This time Ladda speaks, and her words are the most difficult to hear.

The gate swings open and then shut. A waft of charcoal-grilled meat, smokey-sweet chilli, pungent fish sauce, roasted rice, hot plastic bag. A thin, quiet person carries all this towards them, wearing the white shirt and black trousers of a first-year uni student, their hair precisely centre-parted above thick-rimmed glasses on a little beaky nose. When they see the stranger crying in the middle of Caramel's courtyard, they freeze.

'Note, it's okay. This is Fah-sai and Namfon's old friend.' Caramel walks over to help Note with the bags.

It's been a very long day for Note. They have run out of words, so they simply quirk their eyebrow at Caramel.

'Hey, I didn't do anything except give her a haircut. The first one, you know.'

While Caramel goes inside for dishes and cutlery, Note gives Thames a stick of little round grilled sausages. Thames takes it, her eyes moving curiously over Note's face. Note gives her a thumbs up.

*

The restaurant is so chic it's barely lit, distinguished from the velvet night only by its polished surfaces.

When they reach the table, Nipah stares. Pannee forces a smile.

'What have you done?' Nipah asks her daughter.

'It's a haircut,' Pannee strains. 'I like it.'

'I knew I shouldn't have let you go. How could you do this! Did Fah-sai put you up to this? Don't lie to me—I saw the message you sent her about being here. You know, I can send you home at any time and stay here.'

Nipah knows she can rely on this threat to bring her child back to a shared understanding. She feels Thames' defiance slump. But then—

'Fine,' says Thames. 'But let's have dinner first.'

Nipah gasps as if struck, her fingers gripping the edge of the table. Within seconds, she is breathing hard in Thames' face, her grip tightening around her daughter's wrist.

Here we go again … Thames can feel the will seep out of her bones, muscles, pores. She waits for Nipah to drag her through the restaurant, shouting in Thai and English for the benefit of all, as if the world were her personal lakorn.

Last time, Namfon was small, confused and upset, watching her friend's mother powerlessly while Pannee shushed her. This time, she is standing tall beside Thames, and while her hand on Nipah is gentle, her feet are planted like the roots of a tree.

Pannee glances between the two people she loves most in the world. After a moment, she too places her hand on Nipah's shoulder and coaxes her away from Thames. They are all completely silent, their faces tear-streaked.

Namfon puts an arm around Thames and leads her back outside. 'We'll be eating Isan food tonight after all.'

Outside, Wat Arun rises above the Chaophraya, floodlit and proud.

*

srirachini69:
Hey again Fah-sai. I'm sorry about those weird messages. It's just that I'm remembering our trips to Thailand together.
Remember when we found that giant jellyfish on the beach?
You touched it with the edge of your sandal, very gently, just once. The look on your face!
I didn't know something like that could exist, something that could still surprise you.
You seemed to know everything, but acted as if you knew nothing and needed to understand things in your own way.
Is that why you left - to find answers?
You kept telling me things about the world in a way that made my mum really angry. I thought you were wonderful and brave and exciting, and then you were just
Gone.
Maybe the reason why I keep holding on to the space where you were is so I don't have be the brave one.
No, forget all that. Forget about who I want to be. I still want to see you and know how you are.

___skysthelimit:

It's so good to hear from you Thames. I miss you too! Sorry for the delay in getting back to you, was in the middle of the jungle. Been thinking about you a lot. Namfon and that lot have been telling me all about you [*big grin*] I'm in Chiang Mai at the moment but yes, of course we can meet up. [*contented face*]

srirachini69:

This is Thames' mother. You will stop contacting my daughter immediately or I will contact the police as this is harassment, which is a crime. Stay away from my family.

___skysthelimit:

Hello Auntie Nipah! Hope you are well. Respectfully, this is Thames' decision. Have a lovely day. [*slightly smiling face*]

*

> (She is in the dream house again.
> There is a frangipani tree growing in front of her.
> Frangipani, also known as lanthom, like sorrow.
> Nipah snorts. Of course.)

After enduring years of state violence against yourself and your community, you're thinking about how to dream. In particular, how to dream dreams that cannot be seized by power.

You and your friends experiment with making this thing on your phone that will feed on dreams to open up and pierce through perceptions and strata of existence. You cobble knowledge together from forums, gossip and hearsay, programming something that fats itself as your phone lies beside you at night, using your dream as an entry point for you to walk into other people's dreams and gather up material for later. It shouldn't work, but it does. In waking life, there are particular dreamspots, points in reality that are soft, stretchy, sensitive, like skin; here, the dreamstuff stored on your phone can be released, pooling out onto the surface of this plane, melting into a comforting, sticky waking dream. And this dream can be shared, inviting more hands to tenderly pull the material apart like a batch of milk buns, nourishing each person in the creation of their own worlds.

The phone itself is important. It is made with rare metals and labour extracted from the colonised world and holds the residue of your power and activity, living with you so closely and constantly, always in contact with your body and mind, eating endless information and conveying it back to evil private companies; a commodity and a terrible thing and a potent focus. Ladda's desktop rig didn't work nearly as well as that beaten-up, well-loved phone you couldn't bear to replace.

There's that feeling of being watched again. Here you are inside someone else's dream, collecting material from their innermost world, and you don't know if they know what's happening— consent here is murky. None of this is romantic or ethical, but it is one magic available to you right now.

The only people who know about this are you, Ladda, Caramel, Note, Fah-sai, and now Thames. You keep vigil over each other while you dreamwalk, your sleeping bodies flickering in and out of existence. You've got to be really careful with this shit, because it could always fall into the wrong hands (the hands of the state, any state).

(Nipah does not understand any of this.
She seethes.)

You are all here tonight. The dream house has never held so many people before.

Fah-sai is sitting at the bottom of the broken escalator, dipping her toes in the water.

'Thames, I'm so sorry. I shouldn't have left like that, it just ... it had to happen really suddenly.'

'There's nothing to be sorry about. Yeah, I was sad, but it wasn't the thing that made me slam the MENTAL ILLNESS button, you know? It was lots of things all at once and it was everything that was already *going on. It's hard to describe because there's no beginning and end. It's so difficult to be in my body inside a world like this. Just as well we can't stay in this dream together or I ... would escape forever, I think.'*

Fah-sai looks serious. 'We can't turn away. We can use rest and safety to stay present.'

'Can you imagine how organised dreamwalking could link people together?' says Ladda.

Caramel pokes Namfon. 'You'd probably still find a way to avoid answering your messages.'

Note dips a finger into the water, sending beautiful ripples across the surface.

(Nipah wants to scream at them.
She wants her rage to rise up, a great wave crashing down on
their disgusting, happy faces and dissolute bodies.
How could she be tossed aside for people like *that?*
She gave up her whole life for her daughter, her dream, but
Thames has burst free of her.
Nipah needs to be yoked to something—to the Family, to the
Nation—but now, she is cast adrift.)

The dream house starts shaking. The water trembles. The structure starts collapsing.

(She thought their fear would delight her, but she now knows
she is part of the thing hurting them.
She lets herself see all the choices available to her, something
she never does in waking life, where fear is the fast and clear
decision-maker.
But this is a dream, after all ...)

Now she is on the other side of the dream.
She sees all of them clinging to each other
hands-clasped-legs-up scrambling to safety:
they have gone where she can no longer reach them,

her daughter, her heart.
Strange quiet settles over Nipah.
She is in the water as everything is crashing down around her, but
she is completely still,
floating, starfishing.

Nipah wakes up sobbing. Pannee is beside her, wrapping her up, stroking her hair, murmuring things that she needs to hear but struggles to accept.

*

crushedlittlestars:
i miss you.
i've been thinking abt what u said ages ago -
still holding your mum's hand even tho she uses it to hurt you
i've done it too - my stepbrother, my friends, too many of my partners...
i want u to be able to say that she is harming u and it is honestly ok for you to feel hurt & pain & anger
your mum won't be lost forever if you let go of her hand just for one moment
you can want it to stop.
you can want to be treated better.
you can want distance (for now / for ever)
i worry that ur too scared of what i think to tell me how i can be a better friend to you, it's actually such a relief whenever you piss me off cos it means u can talk to me!
[golden heart]
i love you so much. glad u have found even more people who love you in the way you deserve.
i'm gonna try that thing on my phone tonight...
maybe i'll see you in my dreams xx

*

TWO

PICKING AT THE LEFT-OVERS OF 'GRANDMA'S MISPLACED RECIPE FOR CULTURAL AUTHENTICITY'

I have decided to bring in another autobiographical interlude, after much internal debate. The Asian autobiography, the racially melancholic memoir, is the thing that sells, but I have no interest in either sales or self-promotion. Instead, I include my experiences here as a point of relation. Contrary to popular narratives about the motivations of racialised queer authors, I write with the presumption of your disagreement and confusion, not with the expectation of speaking into an echo chamber. And while I write knowing this will appear as a book, not the fleeting unthoughts of online posting, I'm still braced for your sceptical reply. It's embarrassing to have this unreasonable urge to argue with strangers in my head, as if heading off criticisms by wielding my life story like a blunt weapon will achieve anything. I forget that I can start from a place of understanding, that other people's lives can connect to mine.

In 2014, I wrote an article called 'Grandma's Misplaced Recipe for Cultural Authenticity', which was published on *The Toast*, a now defunct American feminist website. The piece explored the legacy of intergenerational abuse, as well as the alienation I felt from conventional narratives about food, heritage and grandmas, the genre of writing that critic Jonathan Nunn has since described as 'nonna porn'.[1] I struggled to contextualise how my grandma was both an incredibly violent person and a great cook. My fee was $50.

This was during the heyday of millennial first-person perspectives on online feminist magazines. Mine was one of many, many posts. It wasn't one of the popular ones; it lacked humour, and I felt the need to be deeply earnest and write in sentences that wafted in the general direction of meaning for a while before deciding to make a point. The navel-gazing in my piece made it essentially the opposite of those viral posts that rigorously eschew self-reflection in favour of shock value. Still, it was meaningful for the handful of people who read and commented, sometimes sharing something of their own stories. It surprised me that nobody complained that I had mined my family's trauma for a piece of writing, or that I had not represented all possible perspectives or distilled a clear solution to the issues I was trying to explore.

Reading it back is embarrassing. I take many thousands of words to conclude that it is actually fine for me not to really like my grandma; she doesn't need to be a feminist icon or source of ancestral wisdom. It's also concerning to see how I shoulder a shocking amount of responsibility for my mother's feelings—I can still feel how holding back all those emotions actually changed my body into something else.

Even as I question the worthiness of my efforts and intentions, I don't regret the piece—it was important for me to learn that I could reach other people with my writing, and they could reach me through their reading. What I did not understand then, however, is that authentic truth-telling on its own does not result in liberation. It is so often said that we should 'speak truth to power', that if we share our stories, we will be free. I still think that can be true, but what's also true is that power doesn't give a damn, or if it does, it responds with the boot heel or a tempting double-edged offer.

Our food is a spectacle for whiteness

The Asian food story comes in many forms. Here, as always, I say 'Asian' to denote the general focus of my thought, not to distinguish an exclusive category with an airtight label. Not only am I uninterested in creating a special Asian club, but I also think the following inquiry applies to many modes of lived experience, and I offer it to you if it's useful.

There is, of course, the historical food story: foodways criss-crossing lands and oceans; family memories and heritage recipes. There are stories from today: how we go to the wet market in the morning; how we commune for big feasts; how we harvest from the land itself. There is the overarching labour narrative: working the fields; working the front and back of takeaways and restaurants; the unpaid activity of keeping households warm, clean and well-fed. The stories live with us. We practise them with every sip of broth or sharpened knife, when we choose which greens or gourds to eat, which aromatics to pound or chop, which foods to get us through sickness and sadness, and whom to sit down to eat with.

But while all these stories can be tantalising, comforting and delicious, when it comes to published food stories, I often think we've already ceded so much to middle-class white people. Questions of representation, authenticity and appropriation are inevitably raised, then neatly answered: give someone of unquestionable *pedigree* (and I do use this word with full and menacing intent) the opportunity to write about their experiences, to represent themself (and, by extension, all people from their culture).

I've noticed how very sensitive details can make their way into our food stories. When shared by people of colour, such details are seen as a peculiarly exotic flavouring, an opening for others to be tourists in our traumatic memories, to feel cultured through pitying us. It doesn't stop there: this style of narration has shaped how many of us now talk about food, race and memory *even to each other*. Think of how The Smelly Lunchbox Story has become its own subgenre in diaspora food writing, elaborating the psychosocial impact of rejection and mockery of your culture by white peers since childhood—the apparently foundational trauma key to understanding The Diasporic Experience. Really, the smelly lunch script narrates a rather specific encounter that is far from universal.

Not everybody has a smelly lunch story, salacious memoir or handed-down family recipe. More importantly, these hot gimmicks aren't reliable measures of the realities of racialised experience—and fighting about which count as authentic gets us nowhere. In the end, picking apart and savouring personal anecdotes and accounts will never offer a full picture of the complex, layered circumstances that structure our lives. This runs absolutely counter to the popular idea that justice is to be gained through divulging trauma as a prerequisite for care (because it's only when seen as *individuals*, each with a unique story of suffering, that oppressed people are made human).

This twisted model of exploitation under the guise of justice and care is commonly peddled by white middle-class editors and writers, as we see in their desperate bids to extract our stories. I want to be clear: the problem is the structure and not a bunch of moustache-twirling villains, but it's also true that the structure of a media industry owned by the rich is maintained by people acting in accordance with their (racial-ised) class interests. Squeezing out and selling racial trauma is expected from them, it's their grift ... but honestly? I think it's also become ours.

Maybe that's uncharitable; some of us rage against what has been thrust upon us, yes, but some of us have become inured to it, or perhaps even enjoy this situation. We fight for scraps, wanting to be anointed the representative of our culture, wanting to win. It's useful for the ruling class to create this competition and commodify certain stories, since it wears both readers and writers into a shape that fits their needs. Barely aware of what's happening, we find that we've internalised the logic they have imposed; in our own conversations with other people of colour, we talk about our struggle against slights and tropes, running in tight circles of the personal without reaching outward into wider contexts and connections. Our archiving and storytelling take place online, where we argue for symbolic resources like hashtag virality, partly because the offline world seems so desolate, partly because our imaginations have been curtailed. We constantly appeal to whiteness— *dear white people!*—and even when we're writing with rage and contempt, we're pleading, *why don't you love us?*

Our food is traumatic for whiteness

While many white people are ravenous for both our cooking and our food stories, food also prompts whiteness to express its disgust, shame and desire for neutralisation. The charge of bland cuisine in particular sets off deep psychological defensiveness in white Brits, even many of those who think of themselves as both class-conscious and anti-racist. Painting themselves as victims, nostalgic for a plain and simple past—with palates to match—they sulkily tweet and grumble about how spices, the spoils of imperialism, were *expensive*. Poking fun at bland cooking then becomes an affront to the working class, while Britain is positioned not as the seat of a rapacious empire but as a wounded nation dominated and mocked by people with more flavourful cuisines.

In Bland Food Discourse, working-class food does not refer to the fare of people caught in particular socioeconomic relations but rather to Ordinary British Whiteness—for some reason embodied by Heinz beans on toast. Any product that doesn't come in a tin or a packet is suspiciously middle-class; the fact that working-class migrants and people of colour might shop at a wet market or 'ethnic' food shops filled with all manner of affordable groceries is completely beyond them. While framed as stemming from the traumas of historical poverty, such grievances in fact rely on the idea of spice as objectively foreign, excessive and threatening, as well as of imperial plunder as burdensome. You don't see the Beans-on-Toast defenders becoming emotional about other colonial goods like tea, sugar or chocolate, yet spice, in all its smells, tastes and colours, is a contagion to them. Of course, this is unless it has been naturalised as *British* spicing: white and black pepper can be found on even the most timid of tables; the faint suggestion of cayenne or paprika is present in innumerable condiments and dishes; nutmeg is used for gentle custard and rice pudding; cloves in pink gammon or mulled wine or bread sauce; ground ginger for parkin and gingerbread; mixed spice for hot cross buns, festive pies and puddings. This style of seasoning has been written into the memory of white Britishness and is somehow untinged with classism—it's just good, wholesome food for good, wholesome people.

Now, I could continue with a little history lesson, perhaps sprinkle in some personal anecdotes (I have some really sad ones that have made nice white people cry), but I don't think this will actually solve the problem. As interesting as it is to learn about family stories, foodways, all the nuances of history; as important as it is to trouble the clean splits between coloniser and colonised, white and racialised, bland and spicy ... all the well-presented narratives, arguments and facts in the world cannot overturn entrenched structural racism. We can try all we like to win white people over by narrating our harrowing experiences and making them love our food, but will their love set us free?

Love our food, love us?

A refrain I've heard from other ESEAs is that white Brits are hypocritical for professing to love Asian culture while maintaining ignorance of, silent complicity with, or even active engagement in anti-Asian racism. We urge white Brits to see this as inconsistent and to bring the 'love' they purportedly feel for our culture into alignment with their actions. It is with love that I wish to highlight that such a strategy is specious, albeit very understandable, since it neither convinces others nor provides us with insight into the dynamic at play.

Let's take a step back: I use the word 'we', but who is really cooking the food that white people love so much, and who is crying for their love? Looking more closely, we see that this 'love our food, love us' rhetoric doesn't come from line cooks, dish-washers or anyone who actually works in food service, but that it's touted by middle-class Asians, like celebrity chefs, food writers and influencers. While they may dream of sitting down to a dinner where bread is broken alongside racial stereotypes, that wish is simply irrelevant to the needs of Asian restaurant workers (particularly those who are undocumented) being exploited by Asian bosses. For many people, racism is not symbolic but material: the state ties work to migration status, and so food service might be the only job available. Some of us are not fighting against image and bias, but to survive.

The appeal for 'love' misses that white people's simultaneous enjoyment of Asian food and indifference to Asian suffering is not dissonant or paradoxical—it is exactly how this system is *meant to work*. If we understand race as constructed through class, we can see how the racialisation of Asians is shaped by the very work of making food. We are somehow both tirelessly robotic and spicily sensual, producing an infinite stream of perfectly seasoned exotic dishes. The professional kitchen is a hot, loud place, where everything has to be faster all the time. It wears down the body, giving us scars and burns, sore backs, knees and elbows, fucked-up sleep patterns. Like so many other workplaces, the kitchen is a site where people are turned into individual mechanised units of skin and muscle, their dreams subordinated to the extraction of value.

In these circumstances, racism isn't a problem of personal feeling. Getting white people to appreciate us because of our food or other cultural 'contributions' won't liberate anybody, nor can it heal, house or feed bodies worn out by work. Love is nice, but labour rights are a better place to start.

Do not beg for crumbs and hope that stories of our hunger will result in a full loaf. Do not ask for a seat at the table; demand to know how it is made and who puts the food on it, and whether they are being fed, too.

*

BETWEEN THE MEAT
AND THE SKIN

I AM THE MONSTER SWIMMING IN THE BROWN MOAT AROUND YOUR WHITE CASTLE

Hello, inky water. I move through your silt, tongue lapping at rusted shopping trolleys and little fish. Hello, grey city. I come up into you fresh and cold, cold like violence, fast and stinging. Hello indeed.

In this stretch of canal, the only light is pollution, greyness gentling nearer the horizon above black-blackness, whispering trees and silent pointed aviary. In this gorgeous shadow, I could be any little nightswimming creature. A coot calls, a comical warble. Its home is a pile of twigs and bits of rubbish tucked in the margins.

My hair trails behind me as I swim, dark and eelish. Below my chin hang my throat, lungs, heart and viscera, all lusciously plump and tight like vine fruit, undulating through the dirty, cold, delicious water. Each night, I shed my outer flesh and go to supper in a place that has a little more character. Haven't you done the same?

A point of white light in the distance. I go just under the surface of the water, watching who comes, peering up among the floating weeds.

A bundled-up artist moves. Small, thin echoes of music surround him as he marks concrete with colour. He is not what I want.

Couples walking two abreast, determined to remain that

way even as the towpath thins. The world must know their couple-form, even if it inconveniences, annoys, threatens to push others out into the water. The couples all look the same. Funny how that happens. They would do for me, but they are like plain congee, and I like my food well-seasoned.

I wait and wait and wait.

Some police appear and I would very much desire to crack them open, split them skin-and-uniform like rambutan. I could, with my one pair of very strong jaws, tackle a deep and persistent problem. A good evening's dinner, but at what cost? A spate of missing pigs just makes the Castle very nervous, prompting it to lash out by engulfing more and more communities, violently closing in and casting blame on the already vulnerable. It is a problem bigger than my hunger alone could solve.

When I do find my dinner, I think about how any one of my meals could be a police officer pretending to be a normal person, that is, a person who isn't empowered to kill other people. It doesn't matter to me, since I'm immune to the badge, the uniform. But it matters to some people, the people I never eat.

I have seen tonight's prey before. By day he is an estate agent, but for the evening he has removed his dark-blue suit and horrible long, brown shoes in favour of an ironic Christmas jumper and Chelsea boots. He wears the same oily grin to work as he does to follow people in the street—mostly women, as you'd expect, sometimes people who look like women, and always people who do not look like him.

I have been waiting to catch him for a while; he does not often come to the canal.

'Oh-whoa-oh-oh!' He slurs the chorus of Peter Andre's hit 'Mysterious Girl' as I come out of the water. I don't really think there's a resemblance between me and Champagne Inthachak, titular girl in the song's 1996 music video, but it is dark, and he is very drunk.

I smile at him and swim a little closer. I am only doing what he's asking me to do.

In the music video, filmed on the beaches of southern Thailand—all palm trees and sand and waterfalls—everyone, Thai and not-Thai, has brown skin and white teeth; everybody and nobody is exotic in this place. Peter Andre, with his Greek Cypriot heritage, has roots somewhere that was once also read through the lens of Orientalism; now he is here as a Westerner, southern Thailand becoming just any tropical holiday, a place with lots of dancing aunties and local children, and exactly one beautiful girl.

The man continues his rendition, crooning that he wants to close the distance between my body and his. There's nothing wrong with that, is there?

The music video is mainly interested in Peter Andre's glistening torso. Peter Andre is mostly interested in dancing with Bubbler Ranx and Ryan Jackson and only interacts with Champagne in the song's last twenty seconds. Champagne is interested in wandering about town, buying three of something from aunties selling bundles of leaves and stink beans, and performing a series of movements in various locations, like in the middle of the street or under a waterfall. She sometimes looks in the direction of the camera, but her actual gaze is far away, unreachable. She is meant to be the object of desire, but she is deeply unavailable—to both us and Peter Andre—for most of the video. The camera lingers on Peter's abs; he is oiled flesh and curtain hair. Champagne fades in and out of each scene like a ghost. She cannot be possessed; she is haunting him.

I come out of the water. The man expects clinging clothes and nipples like walnuts. What he gets is entrails: the sight of mine, and my desire for his.

He tries to flee from all my wonderful teeth. As he begs for his life, I know that he will learn nothing. If he needs to violate people as much as I need to eat, then my task is clear. There will be no great epiphany before my jaws close on him.

*

AN AVERAGE LIFESPAN IS NOT MINE NEVER MINE I WILL NEVER DIE AND I WILL NEVER DIET

My wife and I are very old. With age, we are supposed to be desexed in favour of wisdom, appetites withered. But with each passing decade, we have disarranged ourselves further, become bigger and hungrier. We are monstrous because we were pushed out of womanhood, then actively abandoned it, fleeing from the timeline of cisheterosexuality and thereby achieving a sort of immortality.

The story is told of the young and queer dying, again and again.

The average lifespan of a [   ] is [ ].

Fill in the blanks, again and again.

Against this tide, it seems understandable to swap early death for self-preservation. To lead a straight and narrow life being satisfied with the just-enough, the little wistful sigh and turn of the head. Maybe some of us even argue to be protected in view of our extreme vulnerability, pleading our abjection for pity, asking to be left alone as we continue with our mild, unthreatening existences.

We think this is obscene. We see this as being prevented from our own creation, frightened away from making ourselves and each other, from nurturing our hunger for connection. We know our desires must be answered. If we are hungry, what do we need to nourish ourselves? How do we feed each other? Who is depriving us of what we require, and how do we make them answer for it?

Maybe we *do* want to tear it all down, to destroy Private Property and The Family within.

Maybe we are *not* innocent.

Maybe we *are* violent.

The hunger that gnaws is a problem we will solve together with all of our teeth.

QUEERS BITE BACK!

*

My mother told me that krasue are contagious. That's what they always say, that a monster is catching.

Our neighbour is a krasue! she told me. *I saw her spitting into the soup. She is trying to make more of herself. Child, stay away from her ...*

It was incredible how she thought I could refrain from that most basic of human needs, or that I would be both restrained and discerning enough to identify tainted food during a temple day or festival or celebration.

It didn't escape my notice that our neighbour was a woman who was happy to live alone. My mother disliked her as she thought a woman should grow family on the land around her, unless she was an ascetic who'd retired to the sacred ground of a temple, white-robed and useful to the men in orange. Then again, maybe my mother simply didn't like our neighbour in the same way that she didn't like most women, including her own daughter and, ultimately, herself.

One morning, I woke up with a vicious hunger. I craved something slick and sweet, so I snuck over to a nearby orchard and ate every single mango that hung there, sucking each one down to its funny scalp-seed. The owner gave me the scolding of my life, loudly cursing at me to shit myself to death. At home, my mother cried and came at me with the switch for my unneighbourly ways, but what was a girl to do? I was just so hungry.

That night, I lay there on my sleeping mat, skin stinging, guts churning. My hunger was fresh and strong like a pool heaving with catfish; my emptiness was perversely muscular, as if the walls of my body were contracting. There was, at some point, a moment of such unbearable pressure that I thought the orchard keeper's curse was coming true—but instead of shitting myself to death, I felt a luscious sense of release and found myself light and free, completely at ease.

I went out in the night for dinner.

*

What is a krasue?

Well, some of us say, 'Ah! There is no word to describe what we are.' Others say, 'Oh, but this word describes us perfectly.' Or perhaps they say, 'There is no translation for what I truly am.' Translation is not just a case of success and failure, one chance only. Translation is happening constantly.

Let's translate me as a vampire, though I'm not glitteringly white. A vampire drinks only blood, piercing the milky neck of a maiden who is all tumbling hair and heaving bosom. It lives in a stone castle and wears velvet and burns in the sun. There are rules to a vampire, governing space, appetite and vulnerability. You know the vampire rules because you are told them, and you brush aside the advice because you are very foolish and think that having all your vitality sucked out of you only happens in movies.

The way that I eat blood and guts is not a delicate perforation but a rending open and burrowing in. Sometimes, I admit, I too am involved in tedious heterosexual lovestories. You couldn't ever discover who I am unless I chose to reveal myself to you, since I keep to myself, take care with my skin and am highly practised in managing my strange hungers. There are rules to my existence, too: I hunt at night, slipping back inside my skin with the dawn. If my skin is destroyed, I cannot hide from the sun and will eventually die. You are told the krasue rules and you keep your guard up, because fearing us is part of how your culture is made.

Your fears about me—about tainted food and water, missing livestock and village outcasts—seem far away from the concerns of the White Castle. To describe me as a vampire makes me comprehensible to them, and I can certainly be cast as that type of creature—I look very fetching in frills and velvet. But what does any of this matter to the people who become my food? The urgent issue for them isn't who I am but my teeth in their flesh. You think you want to know exactly what makes me different so you can say, 'Aha!' and defeat me soundly, but that's not what makes difference so interesting. My difference tells you about yourself.

*

Nak sometimes grieves for her first home. Goodness knows why we stay here, but personally, I think it's out of spite and a need to haunt. When her sadness comes on a warm day after the rain, I take her down to the canal. The smells of smokily cooked meat from the market stalls mingle with murky water and petrol and wet stone and jasmine. Though it isn't exactly hot and the jasmine here isn't quite the right cultivar, it feels like we can be in this gorgeously disgusting place. The fragrance of flowers like jasmine and hyacinth and honeysuckle is attractive because there is something low, dirty and faecal that grounds the higher registers of their beauty. They would not be so alluring without a little taint between the petals.

We live in Hampstead Heath, below the Hollow Tree, because the gays here know how to have a good time. Nak brought Ghostbaby with her, but we set them free. You might be able to spot the many Ghostbabies here in winter darkness as they contentedly swim with the waterfowl in the ponds by Kenwood.

Our homemaking need not accommodate a child, only her and me. We burrowed into the earth and have made a cosy hole there, lit by glowing mushrooms and made comfortable by Nak's weavings: dried brambles, reeds and vines from the Heath fashioned into rugs and hangings, surfaces to be formed and filled with dead leaves and made into beds and cushions. It's an ideal place to watch movies. We rigged up a little underground cinema (don't ask how) and spend hours watching my wife's greatest hits and 'Mysterious Girl' on repeat.

I am proud of my love, and so I want to tell you more about her. Nak lived on the banks of the Phra Khanong river in the mid-1800s. She was an ordinary woman, which is the type of woman most vulnerable to becoming a National symbol. A normal woman is created by the Nation; a normal woman possesses a body that can be filled with more of her (future wives) or more of her husband (future soldiers). It is very easy to fail at being a normal woman, but the Nation pretends there is nothing more natural than success and nothing more unnatural, disgusting and inhuman than failure.

Nak died in childbed, but she continued being a Ghostwife with a Ghostbaby, waiting for her husband to come back from the war. She haunted the house, her local area and her man on his return, before being captured and held inside an urn. Her story travelled; she went on to star in tragicomedic ghost stories and became a patron spirit of motherhood. My wife has range. One of her earliest appearances in cinema was *Mae Nak Phra Khanong* (1959) by Rangsi Thatsanaphayak, only twenty minutes long, a choppy black-and-white number with more than a little comedy about it as she antagonises the villagers, fading in and out of each scene like Peter Andre's Mysterious Girl. In Nonzee Nimibutr's *Nang Nak* (1999), she was a wayward ghost who wanted too much and had to be put away by a holy Buddhist patriarch, since a dead womb cannot produce more soldiers or more wives. Nak is also a symbol of a wife's undying love, but she's only really loved back in Pisanthanakun's *Pee Mak Phra Khanong* (2013), in which her husband is a doting babyman ghostwifeguy who adores the embrace of her long, long arms. (I have always loved her back, each and every her.)

There is still a temple in her name, a place for women to pray their sons are not conscripted. In this role, she is called Mother Nak; offerings are made to her and her baby of clothes and toys and make-up. For a time she was content, until one day she wasn't. Her transition was slow and gradual but, being something that existed outside of time, outside of the comforting rubric of karma and moral hierarchies, she was not worried by this. She did not especially dwell on the particularities of existence but came to see herself as an extension of the land, growing with it. Centuries passed through her. She watched the canals swell and shift and recede, the rotting of wood, the passage of iron, the pouring of cement. Humans and non-humans dwelling, working, playing, dying.

At some point, as the meaning of Nation lost its importance to her, she allowed herself to think: *If the world had made it possible for the people around me to help me, perhaps I wouldn't have died. Wombs do not ineluctably bring forth soldiers, wives and death, and I don't think there's anything sinful or magical or wonderful or disgusting or morally superior about the ability to menstruate or gestate or give birth. They are just things a person can do with their body, like eating and shitting and scratching their nose. The Nation said it was important for me to bear a child, yet I only became important when I died doing so, as if my death were a punishment for my failed womanhood, and my significance after death a redemption of the cost of that failure.*

Seeing people treat land as property to pass down through the body of women, she let go of the notion that land can be owned, as well as the idea that ownership is necessary to belong with what she loves. She gave up that manner of affection and became something else.

One day, she tossed herself into a canal and floated on. She came to know the movements of eels and the secrets of oarfish—something about her long limbs was friendly to them. The Phra Khanong canal flows out into the Chao Phraya, the mother river that pushes through the centre of the land into the sea. Sometimes Nak floated in water that was not of this realm but in a place that is slantwise to us, running through a night market with fantastic creatures and a shopping mall criss-crossed with flowing streams. She can't remember how long she spent in the water (being without normal human flesh, she didn't have to worry about prune-fingers), only that when she persuaded herself to return to the land, she came up in Hampstead Pond no. 1.

London once drank from those ponds. Waters springing from the hills of the Heath—the Fleet, Brent, Tyburn, Westbourne and Kilburn—escaped the ground, slippery, mud-thick, life-giving. As they entered the city and humans expected them to carry away their waste, it became necessary to close over these shit-clogged, diseased rivers for the public good. But maybe it's time for them to return. To free all the rivers of London, you'd have to destroy the very ramparts of the White Castle itself. Just imagine: if someone as splendid as Nak could arrive in that body of captured water, what else could flow into your world if we broke down the palace walls and let the tide crash in? Who would you meet? Who might you love?

We met when I was pursuing a snack through the woods. He was on an e-scooter, screaming. She reached out with her long, long arms and snapped his neck, then threw him to me. How funny it was to find something we shared on this cold island. How precious and nourishing.

*

HOW COULD YOU LOVE A MONSTER LIKE ME?

I have always known what I am (hungry) and what I have to offer (appetite).

With my permission, Nak stays home and gently strokes my empty self when I go out for dinner. My wife takes care of me, knowing that I need this sometimes.

She brings the body that I've cast off close to hers, wraps my skin in her long, long arms, lays me down on her weavings. Her touch is firm as she flips me inside out and understands the colour of my desire. I feel her distant mouth on me as my mouth finds the guts of my prey. I am opening up another body while a part of me lies open elsewhere before her, helpless, flat on my back, wanted and wanting.

She likes me filled and satisfied, salty-sweet, wet and tender.

That is what I give to her. That is all I have ever wanted.

*

LET ME SEE YOU
THE 'REAL' YOU

There are few paths for our existence. There is the cleanliness of being a doll of silk or steel, hollow and gorgeous. Or we can be too much flesh, leaking, unruly, swallowing, a wound. Nak's body caused horror because it is both sexual and reproductive and because she wanted too many things. If I birth, I am a vessel, and if I eat, I am a perversion of that vessel. The body of a krasue is wet and open, naked organs slipping free of a woman's form. Where is its womanhood? Where is its gender? I am a woman sometimes, but if you turned me inside out and tried to map precisely *where* I am a woman, you would not succeed; you'd only see that I am raw, thundering red, all hunger and need. The circle of my time on this earth revolves around pleasurable feeding, not labour. My body simply eats, without reproducing things like capitalism and the family and the home and the land and the nation. You still try to read my body like a book, turning each page impatiently to decode what you see, anxious to get to the real me. But there is no skin to peel back, no true form to reveal: I am both the skin and the meat.

I'm probably a feminist nightmare, that is, a nightmare *for* feminists, considering I'm very literally a floating collection of holes and passages: a mouth, a long throat, guts, an anus. A hunger that haunts the land, the foreign teeth in Albion's flesh.

For you, sex and gender exist as points of comparison. It starts off with, *ooh*, that girl is prettier than me. She is better at being a girl. Her skin looks softer, her breasts are incredible, she has hips but is still small. Her voice is lovely. She can cook, she says all the right things, dresses in the right way. And if you make this girl Asian and observe her through the white gaze, she is given a surfeit of femininity to the point where it loops back round and becomes suspicious. She unsettles. She is too smooth, with her *straight*-straight hair and glass skin. It is excessive. Is she even really ...? I am made in opposition, excessively big, hairy, powerful. Is she even really ...?

Of course, there may be some of you who view the land of my origin as the source of this perversity, of gender and sex gone awry, fake smiles, fake bodies, because you need a firm and fixed idea of yourself as rigorously Western, logical, scientific, while I am monstrous, I have all the wrong appendages, my colours are too bright and my smells are too strong and my borders are unforgivably fluid, threatening your own reproduction: you want pure, clean bodies, boy girl boy girl lined up in playgrounds, so you view transition as *the capture and mutilation of children*, but how wrong you are—as though a process of caring for oneself, living with and through one's body, attending so closely to its whole shape, can be compared to how my teeth rip flesh from itself!

I don't want to prove that I too am a person. I want to free myself from the grip of personhood, guts and all.

Maybe all this is empty, like the body I leave behind at night. And yes, maybe I'm only a surface curved into a self, but I'd like to offer that capaciousness to you. Slip my skin on over yours. Does it feel good to inhabit it? Do you like the fantasy of a beautiful thing? What is it like? I want you to tell me. Come closer.

*

ANCESTOR, TRANCESTOR

None of what I'm saying is new; it all comes from the things my friends and I talk about. I am writing for those of us within diasporic queerness who have to resist not only the normative gender-sex structures of whiteness and our heritage cultures but also the lure of a Queer-Inclusive Nation where we can supposedly be happy, free, finally our most authentic selves. Coaxing people into 'accepting' trans or queer people is not something that is interesting to me; I want to use my little claws to dig beyond admittance into the existing social order. I may not be breaking new ground, but I am one among many others turning up the soil so that something else may grow instead, as I go down into the thick, dark, unknowable earth.

1. XX Adult Human Callipers XX

I considered boldly proceeding from trans-led gender abolition, inspired by the legacy of Alyson Escalante's 'Gender Nihilism',[1] but in our current political climate, I must first make it abundantly clear that this is in opposition to transphobic 'gender-critical' ideology. Meaningful gender abolition relies on the destruction of capitalism, while 'gender-criticals' increasingly align themselves with far-right fascists.[2]

As I write, in early 2022, the situation for trans people in the UK is becoming increasingly dangerous. I cannot in good conscience write about gender without acknowledging how the media (including the supposed progressive left) produces constant transphobic coverage and courts rich and famous transphobes. Though a small and ridiculous group of people, they are also organised, powerful and well-resourced and can't simply be dismissed as narrow-minded and unfashionable. At the same time, we must understand that we will never bring them round with well-considered arguments; they are not here to engage with us but to overwhelm and shut us down with comment deluges while recruiting others to their side. A lot of today's discourse consists of cowardly both-sides-objectivity-debate-me bullshit, some of it espoused by people who are explicitly, violently eliminationist. This is the context in which all trans people in the UK, including people of colour, are living today.

Though I use the catch-all term 'transphobes' in this chapter to describe people with trans-eliminationist beliefs, make no mistake: the target of their most extreme violence is trans women and transfeminine people, with other trans and gender-variant identities really being stepping stones for them to trample along this path of attack. This is transmisogyny, a term coined by Julia Serano to describe the intersection of transphobia and misogyny. Cis people and trans people who don't experience transmisogyny become complicit in this form of transphobia not only through overt acts of aggression, but also by attempting to silence trans women advocating for themselves, placing them under heightened suspicion, treating them as intruders who take up too much room, freezing and pushing them out of community spaces, entrenching ideas about 'male' and 'female' socialisation to delegitimise them, and so on.

With this in mind, let's look at how transphobes (TERFs, gender-criticals, whatever you want to call them) theorise ~~gender~~ sex in a way that denies liberation. The dyadic sexed body *just so happens* to fall perfectly into a binary (male or female) and its reproductive characteristics directly link with social roles (man or woman). It is a very sophisticated scientific theory of sexing, where girl-juice (sugar and spice) makes you soft and nice and boy-juice (slugs and snails and puppy dogs' tails) makes you angry and good at sport. Being transgender is supposedly a 'trend' that mutilates 'naturally' sexed bodies, which are the bodies of wholesome fathers, nurturing mothers and innocent children. Man, Woman and Child.

Jules Gill-Peterson has written about how the cisgender normative framework was created only about seventy years ago in response to the failure of science to prove the existence of such a sex binary, a project that involved violent experimentation on the bodies of racialised intersex children.[3] Transphobes obscure this history while carrying on its legacy, intent on removing the bodily autonomy of children who need access to puberty blockers, even if that means also denying children's ability to consent to all other medical procedures. To them, choosing what they see as sexual pleasure instead of reproducing the order of well-behaved citizenry is a transgression, and wrongdoers must be put in their place. In reality, we are failing all children by repressing trans childhood, because in doing so we cast childhood as the mere larval stage of a 'normal' (cis-hetero) life instead of honouring and encouraging it as a time of growth, discovery and learning.

These paranoid practices of discipline and delight in authoritarianism are completely inimical to trans life. Given these stakes, instead of endlessly arguing with transphobes on Twitter, we must look at what is most urgently necessary and get right to the heart of our material struggles. All sites of public and private life are currently hostile to trans existence. There's the home, the workplace, the shelter, the public toilets; high rates of poverty and homelessness; intolerable working conditions; extreme difficulty accessing transition-related physical or mental healthcare, including hormone therapy, and bans on safe methods for self-medication; the obligation that LGBTIQ+ asylum seekers perform and prove their gender and sexuality to the white colonial state—the same state that endangers trans sex workers through criminalisation ... the list goes on.

There is always work being done and always more work to be done. A special shout out to the Outside Project, a community-run LGBTIQ+ homeless shelter organised in the spirit of social anarchism; QueerCare, a vital transfeminine autonomous care organisation; the right lube, which offers sharp, witty criticism of art and transness under capitalism and has built spaces for trans people to talk together; and *oestrogeneration*, an independent online magazine by and for UK-based trans women and transfeminine writers.

We must recognise that we are **well past the point** of asking nicely, carrying out surveys, making and signing petitions. I swear, if I see one more debate about getting an X for non-binary people in passports ...

2. X marks the spot

A monument always points to something else, a desire to fix a moment in time. The meaning of the monument's historical moment is created over and over again as people turn and interact with it, defacing, destroying and re-making. Reactionaries, however, revere the monument as a capital-H piece of History, unchanging and unchangeable. For transphobes, the body becomes a monument to biological sex, invoking the unseen truth of hormone levels and chromosomes. The cis white body becomes stone, all other bodies its dark shadow or unsightly stain. Whiteness as rightness, rationality, the history of the civilised and the modernity that civilises.

You don't have to be white to participate in the project of white nation-building. Our current knowledge systems train our gaze into that of the scientist-overseer-patriarch, who compares and contrasts different groups of people within hierarchies, designating some as useful to the nation, others as unspeakable, extraneous. Sometimes, you hope that people *other* than you are punished.

(Stay with me—I am trying to give insight into how vulnerable some of us could be to TERF recruitment ...)

You may have once had trans friends and lovers and considered yourself an ally or even a trans person yourself. You used to spend a lot of time dunking on TERFs online. They always seem to find you, and they always have time to barrage you with questions and comments.

*For a while, the contemporary liberal trans catechism—**You can just identify as the thing you want: trans women are women, trans men are men, non-binary people are valid!**—worked ... until one day, it didn't. Now, you have questions.*

*How do we even begin to understand a thing like gender? If this thing is a social construct, 'merely made up', then why are gendered violence and resource disparity so very **real**?*

And for some reason, you keep going back to TERF Tumblr or Twitter, because yeah, those people are awful, but they seem to have a detailed answer for everything, and their ideas are everywhere, and maybe they have a point ...

and then, and then ...

*yeah, actually, **maybe** there are simply some innate differences between people? **Maybe** sex is so deep and immutable that it defies the vicissitudes of time? There's probably **some** truth to it. It just seems so **plausible**.*

You're being overwhelmed with information. You don't have the time or energy or ability to read all these books or swipe through dozens of annoying infographics or listen to a fucking podcast. You wish someone would just listen to you rather than jump to correct you. You don't feel like you have choices. All you have is a body that experiences pain and fear.

After a while, it starts to anger you when you see other people of colour enthusing over pre-colonial genderless utopias when you know that your heritage culture also examines the external genital structure of newborn babies and sorts them into 'female' and 'male' sexes, persecuting one category while assigning social power to the other. Biological sex is clearly a true and stable fact, something that has always existed across all cultures throughout all of history, whereas trans people seem to have appeared only now, out of nowhere.

TERFs offer words that feel like clarity and look like reality.

You're not an out-of-touch, middle-aged white person, ignorant of structural oppression; you're a young person of colour, and in fact, your embodied experiences of racism add substance to your new arguments. You know that your body is not an image made of light, a projection that can be switched on and off at will—it is tangible, comprehensible. Physical difference is real, just as you know your skin is a certain shade, your nose a particular shape, your hair a specific texture. **The violability of your body by another is especially, inescapably real.**

So, it obviously, completely and absolutely follows that the organisation of physical differences in relation to resource disparity and violence is also natural and essential. That is, males are naturally large and violent, females are naturally small and vulnerable and at the mercy of males, white people are essentially oppressive and people of colour are essentially oppressed.

Your social role is predetermined. We were just made that way!

And that's how you become a transphobe.

3. That's just how the world works

There is a popular idea of 'gender equality' that really asks for parity in suffering. White middle-class 'gender-critical' women in particular, overcome by defeatism about their oppression under heteronormative patriarchy, feel cheated of power and blame it all on trans people.

Even some of us who don't think of ourselves as TERFs can fall prey to gender-fatalistic essentialism, simply using terms like 'socialisation' or 'conditioning' instead of 'biology', in a similar move to liberal invocations of 'culture' to avoid charged terms like 'race'. Whether the framework rests on biology, socialisation or culture, the argument is invariably that some groups of people are always violent oppressors while others are oppressed victims. These generalisations can be useful for observing or expressing hopelessness about structural injustices that persist despite attempts to effect change. The problem lies in the belief that social differences pre-exist and predetermine reality, rather than being constructed in the first place to justify and reproduce material difference. Such theories reject not only transness but all transformation and new possibilities, stemming the urgent feeling and soaring vision that we will need to really change things.

In light of this, it's outrageous that some of us are politely requesting things like better media representation, sensitivity training for cops, and the expansion of the state's powers to regulate us (more pronoun choices on our documents, more hate crime legislation)—all in line with the neoliberal project. The idea that we, as trans people, but particularly those of us who identify as non-binary, could achieve liberation if only our gender identity were validated by the state is something we need to re-examine. I despair when I see us getting so caught up in celebrating the First Queer to Do a Thing that we mistake trans police officers or enby prison units for signs of progress. We don't seem to understand that we're allowing, authorising, even asking for tighter state control over gender itself. That is the civilisational grammar we've been taught. But what is the dialect we really relate to? Even better, what is the scream, what is the roar?

In their essay 'Gender Capitalism', the right lube urges us to understand that while expression of the individual self can be radical, it is *action* that will move us into liberation.[4] As well as doing what we can and taking what's offered to us to survive under capitalism, we can also feed and house each other, distribute hormones, fight cops. Harry Josephine Giles teaches us that deep care work is the sister of protest militancy.[5] People are starving, hurting, dispossessed. Some of us are setting up homeless shelters and community centres and care networks. I say yes, I say more. And I also say, when do we start setting things on fire?

4. They don't make gender like that these days

The confidence with which many queer people of colour claim queer ancestors worries me. We are exhorted to KNOW OUR QUEER HISTORY—a history which runs in a straight line, already darkly simmering somewhere underneath us, rich with pre-colonial culture and nation; we just need to hit the right seam. We are encouraged to respond to the erasures of the present by confidently pointing to an identifiable lineage, a stable past that makes us legible and fixed (legibility and fixity being highly desirable traits). We say triumphantly, *look, we have always existed, we are part of conventional historical narratives, let us be!* But when those narratives have always served to further nationalist agendas ... why use them?

KNOWING OUR QUEER ANCESTORS involves looking at all historical examples of divergence from gender-sex norms, identified by various names and descriptions of important social roles. We may even mourn the loss of societies that had a place for people whose identities are situated outside of our current norms—yet another richness stolen away by colonialism and Christian hegemony! We have uncovered who is to blame for the gender binary (white colonisers), so now we can present a vision of culturally authentic and highly civilised queer nationhood. Perhaps we even identify with the genders of our ancestors, claiming them for our own in the now, standing defiantly as our true selves in a political landscape of organised white colonial transphobia. But what doesn't quite make it to the surface of these celebrations and grievances, probably because we know it's uncomfortable, is that we're clutching the image of our historical queerness as a utopic state—one of both freedom and vulnerability—partly just to have a way of saying, *look at what we had, we didn't deserve to be colonised*. Our tunnel vision means that when we're offered medical optimisation of the individual in the neoliberal present, we can't seem to imagine anything more freeing for gender-sex than what we see in an idealised pre-colonial past.

I use 'gender-sex' because I am trying to centre the cleavage of 'gender' and 'sex', and by cleavage, I mean both pressing together and hewing apart. I will grudgingly dip my toe into language here: in Thai, there is only 'phet', which means 'sex', the category babies are assigned at birth upon examination of their external genital structures. This may seem horrifically restrictive to queer white liberal Westerners who are by now used to cleanly separating 'sex' from 'gender' to make a gender-bread person, but I take this as an opportunity to look at how gender and sex create each other and to ask questions about what gender-sex is actually for. (Yes, we can do this without thinking biology will save the innocent or terfily obsessing over jawlines and asparagus gametes.)

The line between 'gender' and 'sex' is fraught and fluid; both have been conceived together and are in constant relationship with one another, oozing about even within the same historical-cultural slice of time. Narratives about 'rediscovering' historical queerness often partake in the consignment of intersex people to the margins. Saying this figure was *definitely* a trancestor because they were *definitely* trans and absolutely *not* intersex or gender-non-conforming doesn't actually strengthen our connection to them. Conceptions of bodily and social differences within historical queerness cannot be neatly mapped onto the categories we understand today or plotted onto a timeline of increasingly progressive understanding. Such acts hide how these categories even come to be known and how they work in our society. This yearning for queer national history and its traditional social roles recuses us from thinking about class and capital; it says *These Old Genders Were Good, Weren't They!* without asking how gender-sex organises class-based societies.

We may celebrate venerated trancestors, but their social role was still prescribed—perhaps within a gender ternary rather than a binary, and perhaps with the social intention of restricting the role of people we now understand as intersex.

It should worry us that we're reproducing a logic of an idyll that is spoiled and invaded. It should concern us when community is turned into a symbol, thin as a coin, rather than a set of differences and relations we make through joyful and difficult struggle. We seem to believe we can anchor ourselves in social reality by using historical figures to weigh us down, substantiating our existence. We are, for example, encouraged to repeat, 'The Stonewall riot was started by a Black trans woman,' again and again, in order to show our indebtedness. We may even know her name, Marsha P. Johnson. But constantly invoking her as a symbol for our own purposes (and I am sorry to invoke her to make a point about her invocation ...!) does not result in material resources and meaningful bonds for the Black trans women and fems in our lives; it does not support them with housing, pizza money, bills payments or protection.

If we want to bring up Marsha P. Johnson, Sylvia Rivera, Stormé DeLarverie, Miss Major or any other historical icon, then it should be to remind ourselves of how we need to act; care as not just feeling but action; transness as action; art as action. Icons don't need resources, but there are people in our communities who do need them right now. We have to act to meet their needs and fight against the Nation that organises their neglect. Community and care are not theoretical.

We're looking to History to heal ourselves from History without thinking that maybe it's History itself that's the problem. What are the small 'h' histories, the stories that are not rigid monuments to the Nation but gently shifting networks of knowledge and connection that actively inform our equally malleable present? What if histories do not fix things in place but transform them? What if we wrought histories that made us realise other worlds are possible?

We dream of a Queer Nation, but the Nation is what we must destroy.

5. Things we say to each other that are not really true on a political level but are painful to us on a personal level:

Queerness is a white Western thing.

Queerness is not in our parents' heritage cultures.

Queerness is too complicated for our families to understand.

Queerness is something completely unknown to our families.

We have to choose between our queerness and our heritage cultures / families.

6. Are they, aren't they?

I was well into adulthood when I first met someone who both significantly diverged from gender-sex norms and was Thai. It feels wrong even to talk about this; I frequently doubt my memory. Maybe I made it up, maybe I just met a particularly smooth-faced man that day. Even though I get annoyed with people who plunge headlong into linguistic determinism, I can slightly sympathise with their motivation: it feels uncomfortable to pin my memory down in the gendered terms of English.

We were gathered at my parents' friend's house several years ago. I saw ▮▮▮▮ and thought, *I wish I looked like you*. I was out as non-binary to select friends, had short hair, and sometimes self-consciously dabbled in wearing suits with, I am sorry to say, a bowtie. It was really quite different to how this person exuded masculinity in a simple button-down shirt, hair combed back.

███ was dating one of my parents' friends, a glamorous woman. This shouldn't have been a big deal, but theirs was a rather conservative social set, and I'd never seen a non-cishet couple among them, yet here they both were, completely at ease and being treated just like everyone else. ███ sat with the men, used the very same masculine pronouns. And I think that my mother did say about this person, 'Just *like* a man!'—which is not a thing people normally say about those with access to cis manhood. Possibly.

What I knew for sure was that I found ███ incredibly handsome, which somehow made it more stressful for me that ███ had terrible political opinions. I discovered this when I read a piece of ███'s writing endorsing a strain of philosophy that is seemingly progressive in its explicit opposition to global capitalism but can be summarised as vague advice by Thai royalty to poor people to practise self-restraint and collectively eschew democracy. My parents' friend was from an old noble family and ███ masculinity did not jar against dominant cisheterosexuality; this person had a respectable job and staunchly believed in the nation, religion and the king. No threat to the social order, just a circuitous route back to conservatism.

This was not a situation in which I could demand pronouns in bio, and in my attempts to remember ███, I am evaluating my inchoate impressions of ███ presentation against what I know about Thai gender norms. It is difficult, and I worry this is problematic. If it turns out this person was in fact a cis man, what does that say about me and how I construct gender in my head? Maybe I sensed queerness because I wanted it.

All I can be certain of is that my crush did not share my interests. Isn't that always the way?

7. Genderbread and roses

We can't reach gender utopia without unravelling the relationship between gender and nationalism. How does the nation state arrive at the body through gender? We recognise how ideologically suspect it is to essentialise oppression as being *of* the body, but how does oppression happen *to* bodies?

Gender has always been a way to swell the project of the nation, Britain included. We may not have military conscription in the UK, but joining the army or police force has the spit-shine gloss of patriotic masculinity. There is the promise of patriarchal authority: wear uniforms, join a hierarchical power structure that rejoices in misogyny, racism and queerphobia, inflict violence in the name of public order, and protect private property. The nation makes the most of the liberal turn towards shallow identity politics, too, manipulating the violence of misogyny, racism and queerphobia into new narratives ('I can be a proud Asian lesbian *and* a cop!') and new metrics for recording 'hate crime statistics' to expand state power.

Thailand, to many white queer people, is often pictured as a utopic alternative, a joyful land of escape from the ordered gendered world of the West. Every once in a while, a new post pops up that describes Thailand's purported 'eighteen genders'—various configurations of gender-sex and sexual preferences. We have those in Britain too: t4t, needy pillow princex bottom, very tired bi femme top. I am being slightly facetious, yes, but in any case, I think we can understand these categories to be playful and see that this is a vernacular shaped within the contemporary queer scene. As such, these English terms have a clear purpose, while Thailand's eighteen genders are mystified in order to maintain a mirage of Oriental pecca-dilloes, tropical transness and Asiatic androgynes.

Thai culture is seen by Westerners as being very permissive, with its world-famous queer nightlife, a strong reputation as a destination for high-quality gender-affirming surgeries, and relatively high cultural visibility of queer people, especially trans women and fems. As much as I would like to think this view stems from international queer solidarity, it is inextricable from the Orientalist view of Thailand as a luridly eroticised place that exists for tourists' leisure and spiritual and sexual awakening. It is also very much part of Thailand's image of itself as a nation—'Go Thai Be Free,' says the Thai Tourism Board in a campaign to attract LGBT+ holidaymakers, its website full of attractive couples among glittering buildings and gorgeous beaches, as if Thailand has always and exclusively existed for this purpose.

Every nation invents itself. Thailand has not always been Thailand. Siam became 'Thailand' in 1939; before that, it was a collection of autonomous city-states vying for regional dominance. The region now known as Thailand encompassed Indigenous peoples and settlers within internal and external borders that shifted and overlapped with places currently understood as Cambodia, Myanmar, Laos and Malaysia. The great national myth is that Thailand proudly unified itself to liberate itself from colonisation. It is perhaps more accurate to say that in the early nineteenth century, Siamese monarchs colluded with the British to carry out their own colonising project.[6] By the 1930s, Thailand was consolidating its modern self, a nation state featuring Bangkok as its centre and military and police as its armour of coercion, replacing local rulers with appointed officials and protecting the sovereign body from external threats, be they physical or ideological.[7] *Go Thai Be Free!*

Thailand has the draft, demanding tens of thousands of men join the army each year as one of the pillars of nation-building. People who are assigned male at birth are required to turn up to a lottery draw that determines whether or not they will be conscripted. Thailand needs an army in order to continue its military regime, securing Thailand's borders by suppressing Malay Muslim insurgent groups in the south and 'civilising' Indigenous people.[8] If rich people can send their children away from the grip of the military and stump up cash bribes so their sons don't have to serve, who do you think is sucked into the ranks?

Across the world, the regime of the gender binary makes trans women hypervisible and thus vulnerable to violence.

In Thailand, not only are trans women obliged to attend the lottery draw in person, a process that frequently subjects them to humiliation and harassment, but this has become an annual media spectacle, with images of named trans women circulated online, extending the scope and scale of their abuse.[9] While trans women are exempt from military service, such exemption can only be obtained through proof of undergoing tightly gatekept medical interventions for 'gender identity disorders'. This should sound familiar to us in the West; if we wish to access transition-related healthcare or change our identity documents, we must also jump through hoops to receive the medical diagnosis of 'gender dysphoria'.

I focus on trans women not to single them out, but because I was unable to find any information about trans men and transmasc and non-binary people with regard to conscription. This is not to say nobody is talking about it—it's just that I am not in those circles. The popular Thai queer social media websites, accounts, hashtags, magazines and books where people might discuss those experiences are all unknown to me. Writing all this made me realise my un-Thainess: I don't have connections to any queer community in Thailand; if I tried to reach out, I am sure I would just be an imposition, alien and irritating, just another gawking Westerner wanting to absorb as much information as possible while knowing that I have absolutely nothing to offer in return. (I feel this way only about myself, not diaspora in general. I know I should be talking about what I owe to the community, the ties that bind us, my responsibility to them. Please allow me this moment of self-indulgence.)

The West (which includes irritating diaspora like me) tends to collapse our international siblings into simple models of victimisation or righteous forging ahead on a linear time-line to gain rights. It's important to note that the Thai trans community, just like any other group, disagrees on how to fight for liberation. Some want to abolish the draft altogether, while others don't see a problem with the army but just wish it handled gender better.[10] Some are in favour of pursuing a Westernised, highly regulated medical model of gender dysphoria but without the pathology and stigma of mental illness, while others fight for self-determination of gender expression.[11] I hope we can see the points where we could connect in solidarity and continue building global networks.

8. ??????

I use the term 'non-binary' about myself since I'm living within a Western system of gender. For me, there is no straightforward Thai translation for 'non-binary' gender in the linguistic or social sense. There are other Thai people who look like me and are in relationships like mine and who may even describe their relationship to gender-sex in similar ways to me, but they might choose a label I would reject for myself. I am not especially bothered by this. It perplexes me when white queers get upset at the simple observation that 'non-binary' is not a coherent social category—isn't that the point? We want to proceed from multiplicity, not a gender ternary made up of man, woman and an intermediary that negotiates between the two. We have to recognise the incoherence of non-binary so we can agitate for our diverse and varying needs and desires; it is another way to grasp things all at once.

I want to note, too, that given all our different positions and relations, there is also no hard line between 'binary' trans people and 'non-binary' trans people, and that the former don't have straightforward and absolute privilege over the latter. If we want to do things other than win online arguments, it's time we stop using a reductive model of privilege that couldn't possibly describe our complex and at times contradictory social identities. We put so much effort into trying to stabilise our gender instead of *de*-stabilising cisheteronormativity. Some of us even complain that we're just normal people who want to fit in, but considering the fabric of society is built on division and exploitation, why would it be a good thing to fit into it?

I'm not saying it's wrong to feel connected to historical figures or to our own culture, or to feel attached to the embodiment, practices and materiality of gender as we know it. I would be very worried if we wanted to do the thing we think of as gender 'correctly'. What I have been picking at is the attempt to narrow and mould our most generous embodiments of transness and our expansive dreams of gender into something rigid and useful. The deep, caring relationship you have with your body-mind and the feeling of connection it brings to others, whether someone you deem an ancestor or people in your community, are what's most important here. And that doesn't need to be held by the idea of the progressive nation state; it can burst free, flowing into a borderless world.

*

TRANS POWER, MAKE-UP!

Cake wants to be a Magical Girl.

She's about the right age for it. Never mind that she's not actually from Tokyo and doesn't feel particularly moved to protect its communities and infrastructure from intergalactic, interdimensional or criminal threats. These stories don't work in literal terms: you can be an unusually reclusive Thai girl from Croydon and want to be a Magical Girl.

Cake is not alone in this attitude. She has convinced herself she isn't a creepy weeaboo because she herself is Asian and is emphatically proud of being Thai. Japanese culture just has a special allure; Japaneseness is aesthetic discipline, cute and clean and anciently modern. Thainess is what she has to live through, all the messy contradictions and tiresome rules and worrying histories. Japaneseness is an escape from Thainess without abandoning Asianness.

One of Cake's treasured possessions from a rare trip to Bangkok is an instant-noodle wrapper with her two favourite Magical Girls on it. She can't explain why she is attached to what is essentially a piece of rubbish, nor can she explain why the character she likes best is the Magical Girl-Boy with short hair, a deep voice and a fast car.

The Magical Girls on the ramen packet share something with the girls on the Bangkok billboards: they are smooth, neat and pink. Cake is damply brown. Most of the people in Bangkok are the same colour, if not darker; some of the people in Croydon are the same colour, if not darker, and most of them are not Asian in the way Cake is.

Back in England, people ask her where she's from. She wants to say The Internet. She has epidermally failed at racial belonging and wants to exist as an avatar, clean as a pixel, away from sticky fleshed-out life. Her latest obsession is collecting GIFs of Magical Girl transformation scenes, loading them up in a program so she can examine them frame by frame. It feels *good* to do this, a hundred levels up from scribbling in MS Paint and filling in the negative spaces; everything loops so beautifully, you can see what's happening all at once. Yes, this is how girls become Magical Girls.

*

Her dream will come true by the late 2020s. She will be a famous Magical Girl with a perfect, shining face. It will be called a holo mask: filters enclosing the face in a few taps, the glowing non-surface of cyber-existence. This barrier of light will start as a form of protection against the miasma that will beleaguer daily life in the early years of the decade. Only the rich areas will invest in installing infrastructure for air purification; everyone else will have to take their chances during the plague's seasonal peaks, managing with an erratic supply of DIY health products.

The Department of Health will recommend creating a personalised atmosphere using a headset coated with photo-catalytic titanium dioxide and illuminated by skin-friendly UVC-LEDs, along with a portable bipolar ioniser, HEPA filter, absorbent carbon filter, and anti-microbial copper mesh. What will be made available to most people is a thin film of filtration mesh and some purifying light that may or may not damage the skin. It will be just enough to make a screen for projecting the in-built face hologram. Costs will be subsidised by the government in exchange for facial capture—how else will they protect you? Holo masks for health will proliferate, and holo masks for beauty soon follow.

You could look like anything or anyone, but there's a certain face in vogue. The most popular face filter has a full mouth and little nose and eyes that are large but with a certain tilt. Maybe it doesn't look *Asian*-Asian, but it looks racially non-specific in a way that is somehow, paradoxically, also Asian—an Asianness that speaks of obsessive technology, a robot being a sort of doll which belongs to the same fantasy of a beautiful empty object as a cheongsam in a shop window or a curved ginger jar.

If Cake wanted that type of beauty as a teenager, she would have to painstakingly photoshop herself—that sort-of Asian skin has to be so taut that it repels the concept of time itself. Twenty-twenties teens will monetise audiences of millions; in the late 2000s, teenage Cake is content with taking blurry photos of herself in the bathroom and posting them on a forum full of weird men. There isn't really much to do in Croydon, but the online world is boundless.

Between the ages of eleven and fifteen, her days follow a regular schedule:

07.30–16.00: school in a dreary suburb;

16.12–17.12: hour-long nap, except on days when she goes to the library or Forbidden Planet;

17.30–00.00: ignore parents, do homework, have a bit of dinner, pursue online obsessions: accumulating images, writing fanfic, logging on to random chatrooms and talking to random men.

THERE ARE NO GIRLS ON THE INTERNET, say the forum-dwellers, who have the same nerdy hobbies as Cake, only they fling around more money and racial slurs. Cake thinks it's funny that in order to be a girl, she has to constantly say so. She should be repulsed and feel threatened by them, but instead she feels a mix of contempt and camaraderie: as established, she is *not* a sad weeaboo like these horrible white men, but she *is* similarly awful. Everyone is secretly like this, she's sure of it. Everyone is openly disgusting here and she likes that, because she's disgusting too. It isn't safe here, but it *feels* like it is, and that's enough for her.

Writing fanfic isn't that different to having cybersex. She feels smug that she knows all the words to make men excited. She is typing and watching and collecting herself into the person she is going to be; it seems there is only one path, towards men and their manhood.

*

Croydon has always been a bit shit. The council and its chums, land developers, have spent decades trying to chop it up and make it more attractive; Croydon remains not-quite and in-between. Its chief attractions are its proximity to and ability to pretend to be central London. If Bangkok is the Venice of the East, Croydon is the film set of the world, offering its concrete architecture to the screen, its urban decay as a backdrop for other people's stories. Cake assumes she will live somewhere else when she grows up.

But there is a funny bendy bit of Croydon that's still of interest to her: the Clocktower has a library with a good fiction selection, and round the corner is a tiny walk-in medical centre, where, if she had a spare hour, she could get a three-month supply of hormonal birth control. She goes there a few months after turning sixteen because she's bored of always having to prepare for anal, which she only tried in the first place since everyone talked about how taboo it was. She thought it was just a bit of fun, but that isn't how boys see it—she has been marked as someone who's up for it. It turns out this was different to laughing at men who log on to chat to EasternPromise69.

Microgynon, tiny little beige pills in blister packs. Actives: Levonorgestrel 150 mcg, Ethinylestradiol 30 mcg. Synthetic versions of oestrogen and progesterone. One sugar-coated pill a day overrides the menstrual cycle and prevents ovula-tion. On the one hand, it slightly increases your chance of getting some types of cancer and blood clots. On the other, it slightly decreases your chance of getting other types of cancer, your period becomes lighter and more regular, and your skin improves.

The change is slow but sure. Cake finally feels like she's being a proper girl, which she understands involves being desired in a certain way, as delicate, less ugly.

Right before the first time she has non-anal sex with a boy, he leans in and whispers: *Are you on the pill?*

She watches rather than feels him going in and out, arranging and folding her like a deckchair. When she tries to show him what she likes, he goes soft, pouts, and tells her to leave when she starts laughing. She has never felt so humiliated. This was supposed to be actual sex! This was supposed to be normal and enjoyable! She wipes herself off and gets dressed. Maybe the delicacy she dreamed of will never be an option.

*

The one thing Cake has going for her is that she is reliable and organised. She can always put herself in the right place at the right time. Things just line up for her. It comes in useful for arranging events, and that's how she finally finds a modicum of social acceptance—she can somehow insinuate herself into a circle and organise a great party. This serves her well when she gets to university; she isn't especially good company, but some of that glamour rubs off on her. With a newfound average prettiness and an ability to mimic what is pleasing, Cake shifts into a new sphere of life—especially when she starts organising Feminist Events.

She has learned a bit about Feminism and things like that in her lectures. Sometimes, female celebrities say things about Feminism which make them seem cool and funny and strong. Feminism is about girl power; Feminism is a way to actually be a Magical Girl.

Everything opens up to her. She is living in Central and making things happen! With all this new language to describe her experiences, she feels a clench of panic when she realises that she has sometimes behaved problematically and wanted problematic things and had problematic thoughts. To make herself feel better, she often calls other people out—celebrities and random people online—or goes to protests and complains when problematic rioters spoil everything.

Men! Violence is a male thing and males are the problem. *Men!* Cake starts off thinking that it's important to say that Not All Men are bad, but she quickly realises that she really does Hate All Men. When Cake looks at the men around her, she feels a strange ache, she thinks about how small she is in comparison, how broad their shoulders are, and their sharp jawlines, and oh, the backs of their necks, and how stupid and squeaky her own voice is, and—well, it's probably just social conditioning to hate her own female body. *Men!*

Sometimes, when she has been posting a lot, her temples throb with freshly awakened sisterly solidarity. She hopes that nobody ever finds out about her earlier online life; that would mean she was no longer innocent, no longer worthy of protection.

*

The perfect opportunity for Cake arrives in her inbox. An Agency wants to know if she's interested in being part of their latest Campaign? It's about empowering women of colour to fight back. Whose streets? Our streets! Capture the energy of all those protests and put it to use, protecting your people, taking a stand.

It's 2026 and the Tories are no longer in power, having been narrowly beaten by the Greens, Lib Dems and Labour circle-jerking themselves into Green Market Socialists. Everything is better now! We've aimed for the stars, and the economy is a constellation of variations on John Lewis & Partners. Misogyny is now a hate crime, because we've learned that small frail women need to be protected from male violence with big strong laws. The police have listened to women's concerns, instituting numerous reforms with big weapons budgets and recruitment drives. But there is still a public relations problem; the Agency says it's a drain on resources if the police have to keep giving press conferences to talk about how this rapist or that murderer wasn't one of them. The Agency says Cake can help restore trust and keep her community safe. That's how women can take back these streets!

There are growing numbers of unbeautiful vigilante gangs wandering about. They wear ugly masks and dress any old how in clashing colours like pink and black, and they're not trained authorities, but they think they can monitor and criticise police officers. Cake isn't one of them, is she?

The Agency can offer her a salary, a specially made costume. Anything she wants. Anything for the community.

*

She's settled into a routine. She's set her activation protocol to *Community Power, Make-Up!* with one elbow back and fist pumped, the other arm raised high with fingers splayed—wouldn't you, if you'd grown up with anime? Who doesn't want to save the world and be important and beautiful? She has never been more popular. People love how she represents her community as a strong Asian female role model. She has a #CakeSquad, and she sort of knows other influencers, but they're also her competition. At least she looks good. Everyone imitates her: chunky plastic boots, a short-skirted sailor uniform with a big bow and a faceted jewel heart on her chest, ribbon choker, huge lashes, pearls and rhinestones gleaming on her face, all in pink pink pink because she has finally reclaimed her femininity. She walks in a cloud of Gucci Envy Me, leaving a soft trail of fruit and pink blooms in her wake as she hands out sweet justice. One of her most hearted videos is a flour-ishing demonstration of her custom-made pink and sparkly expandable baton against the soft oohs and aahs of *Sailor Moon* background music. Not your submissive lotus blossom: this girl fights back!

Beauty, power, elegance, grace. She is finally the Magical Girl of her dreams.

*

Leaked promo reel for The Campaign. Posted 19 Aug. 2026 by pinkandblackproject.

A young woman is walking alone in the dark, holding a phone aloft. Her mouth moves fast as she speaks in a hoarse whisper. City lights streak overhead. She moves closer; we can see her skin is glowing and smooth, ornate make-up glittering around improbably large eyes. We can't quite hear what she's saying.

The girl glances pointedly over her shoulder, displaying her gleam-ing choker and sailor collar to the camera.

MAN [*shouting from off-screen*]: Alright, darling? [*kissing noise*]

GIRL: … and we're told it's normal, or it's a compliment. But it's not. It's actually a hate crime. And we have ways of—of dealing with that.

MAN [*still shouting from off-screen, but now he sounds closer*]: Where you going, beautiful? Why don't you come over here?

The girl smiles and wags a finger at her phone.

GIRL: Maybe I will.

She puts her phone away and makes a signal with her hand. A shuffle, a distant gleam, indicates another cameraperson is there.

A ball of light forms at the tip of the girl's index finger. She wheels around and points it at the man following her, who shouts and collapses on the ground as sharp brightness lances through him. The girl stands strong and triumphant in an attractive pose. This all happens in less than two seconds.

GIRL: Being part of the Campaign means you are part of keeping everybody safe. Apply now at community campaign dot gov dot UK—

She is interrupted by shouting voices, rising in unity.

VOICES: FUCK COPS!

GIRL: What? Oh my god, ohmygod—

Blurs and swirls. We're up close now. The man on the ground sits up, confused. The camera pans wildly to show figures in pink and black running all around the girl, smeary city lights, sounds of jeering and shouting. The girl is left behind.

People emerge from hiding nearby, some of them with more film equipment, and the girl hangs her head.

*

Cake doesn't want to be a Magical Girl anymore.

People think it's easy just to open the app and run around a bit and then dump the enemy in front of a police station. If only they knew how hard she works, how much disruption she has to put up with from ugly people who are making other people feel unsafe! She tries to tell them in her livestreams, the in-built filter making her eyes glitter with tears that stream prettily down her cheeks. In one reel she fights off her double-glued lashes and melted make-up, showing how her skin doesn't actually glow, her waist isn't really that small, her legs aren't quite so skinny, she barely eats. The heroine-who-is-also-an-innocent-victim content gets a lot of engagement.

Cake really does work, and so does the Campaign. She doesn't really know *how* it works, but she knows it does, and she wishes that it didn't run so smoothly and involve so much admin. She makes enough to live alone and goes days without speaking to anyone, except for the camera team and the service workers who deliver her food and clean her flat. There's just no time for anything else. Every day, more work, more emails, more notifications. Every day, she rolls over, scrolls through Instagram until her hand cramps, showers and gets dressed, fights crime, films sponcon, fills out forms.

There are seemingly innumerable companies that supply the Campaign with products: rape whistles, therapy services, snack boxes, skincare. She was even in talks with a start-up about having a body cam hidden in her choker, but she got uncomfortable for some reason. That happens a lot these days. She is sick of constantly watching and being watched. Her features exhaust her; she examines them obsessively, worrying about the soft corner of her jawline, feeling like an incel. She hates looking down at her body, except on the occasions where she wears a sports bra and it feels better. Maybe ... no. A binder is too far. If she started doing that, then she might start wanting other things. (She doesn't have a problem with the transes. There are actually many of them in her #CakeSquad, so she has read a lot of infographics and is now an ally. Besides, this discomfort can't possibly be transness, which is about revealing your true innate forever self, it's insulting to trans people to compare her unease to their experiences of suffering, because that's what transness is, suffering—real, actual suffering. It's unimaginable to be trans. She won't let herself think about it anymore.)

She can't understand it—she has everything she is allowed to want and she hates it, but she can't stop.

*

One day, Cake receives a message from someone whose display pic is a drawing of a dog with the word 'NO' on its head.

How can you say u stand for liberation when yr colluding w the home office, GCHQ, and the met?? I hope yr open to dialogue about this?

Cake blinks at her phone, then scrolls up to see whether Dog with NO has contacted her before. Her message history just shows a few admiring reactions to her selfies. She checks the profile. *If Nancy Cunard was a* [cigarette]. *Lambrini anarchist, any pronouns.* [Pink heart, black heart.]

Could this person be one of those vigilantes? No. Whoever it is mainly posts about what he (?) or she (???) reads (how many books on the Spanish Civil War does any one person need?). People like that sit around debating ideas, they don't bother going out on the street to serve the community like she does. Scrolling further, she notices that Dog with NO only takes selfies with an ugly non-holo mask and sunglasses, which is a little odd. In one picture she catches just a glimpse of jawline and long-faded green hair, and a hot, strange feeling sizzles somewhere between her diaphragm and groin.

She opens the message again and bites her lip. This is the first time anyone has asked her a question like this; she is more used to being criticised for using a problematic make-up brand. She guesses Dog with NO means that the people who run the Agency are ... problematic? She doesn't really get it, but she knows she's being called out or cancelled or whatever. She consults the FAQ she was given when she joined.

Thanks for your message, she writes back. *I understand your concerns. Everyone fights in their own way, even if we disagree on tactics, we all want the same thing, to be safe and protected.*

Omg haha yeah i've heard that before, replies Dog with NO. *So yr even doing PR for them?*

Cake feels like she is filled with wasps. It's a sore spot that the PR person for the region's community police influencer squad never seems to have time for her.

The typing bubble appears, disappears, re-appears. Finally, a message: *Thing is i don't think we want the same thing. I want to be free. And the saddest part is, i dont think you actually understand what the problem is, there's just too much to explain.*

She would usually block Dog with NO at this point, but for some reason, she really wants to win.

I am shaking right now, she replies. *As a queer mentally ill daughter of hardworking Asian immigrants, I very much understand the problem.*

Ok. Then tell me what it is. Dog with NO waits.

GIRL-HATE, writes Cake, triumphantly tapping out each word. *I think what you're doing right now is lateral violence!*

Dog with NO starts typing, then stops for a full two minutes, before returning to say: *We're done here.*

It doesn't take long for screenshots of Dog with NO's conversation with Cake to start appearing on her feed.

And that's it. Cake tries to carry on, but her followers are dropping like flies. Everyone suddenly wants to let her know she's unacceptable. It's never white men who get stuck with shit like this, she thinks. God, there are so many of them slating her now, as if they're totally separate from the violence!

She posts an accountability statement using all the right words to blame herself and make everyone stop hating her, but the condemnations continue.

Hand over your account to someone else who deserves the platform. *yeah she always gave me a bad vibe. Haha I can't believe this bitch turned out to be an SJW and got cancelled. SAILOR SMOL BEAN IS CANCELLED. we've tried to talk to her about what she does for years and years and she always fucking ignores us...she has no real materialist politics.* **Hand over your account.**

i knew her from some forums, she's fucked up - she instigated this whole dogpile on my friend, i don't feel sorry for her at all. We the members of the Radical Voices Content Creator Union condemn anyone who works with this Campaign. loool her whole brand was always just so cringe. can u believe she's in her 30s and obsessed w animu shit? lmao. **Give up your platform.**

Cake keeps posting. She reads and shares everything Tangerine Freya says—all those simple statements in bold letters are like a nice big wall she can scramble up to make it through to the other side where she will be untouchable again. Tangerine Freya, uploader of wisdom and saviour of the cancelled! *The ways we police each other are the most harmful kinds of policing*, they say between self-affirming quotes and hot selfies, *we must remember that nobody deserves to be punished.* Cake takes this to heart. She may be a community police influencer, but Dog with NO is actually the one policing her!

That feeling is back again, humming inside her, a frenzied, unnameable wanting. She wants it harden into something definite, something she can wield against someone else, and is on the cusp of posting some very nasty things about Dog with NO when they message her one last time.

Hey. Just wanna say i regret posting our conversation. I only have like 12 followers and i'm hardly on here, i underestimated how it would spin out of control. You really pissed me off tbh but none of this actually helps anyone. I guess the conclusion here is that posting is bad... You know posting won't fix this, right?

Cake waits. It is excruciating.

But maybe it's scary for you to not be the main character. Do what you want, but you should get a new phone and a new number and keep a low profile for a while. Ditch those holo face filters you love so much. You have no idea what The Agency has done with yr info. I can't fucking believe you willingly gave them your face. Idk why i'm even messaging you cos you won't listen lmao. Idk idk i just thought u were cute.

She breathes out.

Cake deletes her profiles and changes her number. She could say she didn't want to hand over her account to someone more deserving because she's worried about the Agency—the PR person finally has time for her and is ringing her all day—but really, she just wants to have had something no one else can have.

There is still a part of her that wants to hang on to it all. She joins an Online Community for the Formerly Cancelled, and for a while it's good, really good. In the embrace of such a community, every thought she has is valid, all her feelings important. *Remember: the cancellers' call for accountability is cruelty*, reads a typical contribution on the group, and it is a relief for her to hear it like that. But another variety of post seems to pop up way too often, things like, *I can't believe my life was ruined because of these sexual assault accusations! Fuck weaponised accountability!* She gets that funny feeling again, a furious sense of wanting—she doesn't quite know what she wants but it is not this, it is absolutely anything but this.

She returns to the quiet obsessiveness of her childhood, when she would spend long days in near-total silence learning how Magical Girls are made, except instead of making GIFs she tries reading books, and when that doesn't work she finds other things, videos and podcasts in which people patiently unmake the world, spooling out alternative futures before her. Sometimes she spends days on end streaming this content, lying in bed as if fixed in place, not taking much in. Occasionally she goes outside to try a lecture or reading group, slumping in the corner in loose clothing, wearing an elaborate non-holo mask with full goggles and a hat, never saying a word. Nobody ever recognises her. Cake thinks about how long it's been since she actually spoke to another person. She hasn't heard her own voice since she made her last sponcon clip ... what more does she have to say? Who would listen?

She thinks she understands now. Everyone is harmful, including her, so she is as innocent as everyone else. And that's all she ever wanted.

*

A number of things become clear to Cake once she stops trying to be a Magical Girl.

Cake is a boy.

He wakes up one day and chooses this. It's something that actually feels like his, even though it's difficult to grasp.

If he wants to officially go on T and explore surgery options, it won't be an afternoon down at the walk-in clinic. The Gender Clinic's funding has been increased again, and we even have non-binary legal recognition now, thanks to all that campaigning by neeky bowtie queers working in defence procurement and open-minded Home Office soft-power gays, but it still takes years to get transition-related healthcare on what's left of the NHS. For what Cake wants to access, he would first need to undergo years of prodding questions by Gender Gatekeepers about how he wanks in order to be medically diagnosed with Gender. Since re-learning how to eat, Cake has gradually settled into glorious roundness, and this, too, would be wielded against him if he sought surgery. Gender is only acceptable if it is moulded into thin, fit, useful bodies.

There is more Gender than ever, but instead of Gender abundance, there is artificial Gender scarcity, fierce Gender competition and rampant Gender capitalism. There has been a boom in private companies offering hormones and surgery, gender coaches, trans influencers. *Optimise your results! Speed-run your transition!* If transness is not wretched suffering, then it must be productive, as all gender must perform in the market.

One day, Cake messages a cute gender coach to ask if any of their services are available for free, since he is trying to exist in London but would prefer not to be destitute if he can help it. He is referred to the coach's FAQ, which states that non-profit structures are problematic and colonial and so they have registered themself as a private company, and paying them is only fair, and here's how you can earn some extra money, by the way. When Cake says no thank you, they argue, and later they match with each other on a dating app and meet for a satisfying hate-fuck.

Eventually, Cake finds a Discord of trans people who support each other to self-med. He messes up often, annoys people a lot, and has never felt safer or more held. Sometimes you just need someone who loves you to say, *man, shut the fuck up*. It's not easy to find places like this, where he can be. Though he tries to stay off Instagram, he is still occasionally recognised and treated with suspicion. But sometimes, people's kindness surprises him: a very tired bi femme lawyer with a soft spot for stupid trans boys sorts out his paperwork. It's difficult to keep up with all the identity documentation needed for basic survival; the smallest discrepancy means he has to spend several afternoons battling a phone tree. The only reason he makes a Twitter account is to shout at companies that have the biggest floats at London Pride but spend the rest of the year ensuring that he is cold, hungry and on the brink of homelessness. Journalists want to speak with him when this happens, since that kind of piece always gets huge engagement by gender-criticals, but with the firm encouragement of his friends, he turns down all media opportunities. One day, when he forgets to top up the electricity, he thinks bitterly that only some people can afford to withdraw comfortably from public life.

There are some spaces and groups that he'll never have access to. It hurts, but he has come to understand that he can either harden his entire personality around his pain or focus on action, on doing what is needed with and through that pain, still finding connection where he can.

*

Gender-criticals have become even more radicalised. It's not enough that their grift has extra sauce now that they posture as an aggrieved minority confronting state-supported Gender.

Anything less than total trans elimination is not enough. Affronted by their failure to make the state legislate about sex difference, consent and public space in their preferred terms, they have formed their own vigilante group, whose logo is four callipers arranged in an XX. In every room, every school, refuge and office, there's a woman who quietly murmurs that she's just so concerned about the children or the service users, she's so very worried about male violence and female low self-esteem, about how you're not even allowed to talk about women's problems anymore. In her work, she just wants to help put things right again ... (a tug here or a push there to force a difficult person out, a strict set of policies to keep the wrong sorts of people in line) ... yes, she just wants to understand and support everyone. In the evenings, she posts streams of invective railing against the diktats of a tiny minority of Gender extremists; more and more she goes out on the street, screaming about sex-based rights, violently attacking counter-protesters. These women have become more than a fringe group: they are a consumer identity. The Agency still peddles rape alarms on social media, but now it spins them as specifically for use on intruders in women's toilets.

It feels hollow and self-serving to Cake to laugh at them, considering his history. Instead, he joins the Pink & Black vigilantes that he once despised. After considerable mentoring, voting and discussion, he starts organising with an offshoot of a local copwatch patrol that ensures public bathrooms are safe for everyone.

He has some time before his shift starts. On a whim, he walks to the old site of the Marble Arch Mound, a spectacular failure of a hill from years ago that cost six million actual British pounds to construct and another ten per cent of that to promptly tear down. H., always generous with her knowledge, told him it was built on the spot of the Tyburn Tree, where people were hanged for the crime of being poor and for an afternoon's entertainment.

Croydon looks a lot like this now, a heart full of hard angles, metal frames, faceted glass, architecture that makes space for money and not people. Sometimes Cake goes back to have dinner with his parents, who have never really understood his needs but still feed him well—they'd rather have a son who talks to them than a daughter who is never there.

He looks around at all the buildings, the flow of shoppers, the gleam of windows, the rustle of leaves. A cloud swiftly covers the sun, and everything dulls, softly washed over with blue. He thinks of South London whenever the light is like this. He can't explain why, but Croydon is a time for him, not just a place. It's not quite nostalgia or grief or homesickness. He misses it achingly, but he is so glad to be gone.

*

AN INJURY TO ONE

Testimony of Fungus no. 1, from fragments found scratched into the underside of particularly large Artist's brackets [transcribed by Pimsuk Evernia, queer mycologist] [YEAR UNKNOWN]:

Push
Push through
Swollen / wet / fruiting body
we are closer to you than plants
and we are utterly beyond you—remember
this when you
pick and slice
itch and weep
butter and eat
our tender chitin

We narrate this beyond time. Events branching out, map-like, but not the map which constricts and carves up the world: a map that expands ever onwards, root-hyphae-rhizome criss-crossing, tangling, doubling back.

We have always lived in the walls and edges of the world, emerging at the vertex between piss-stained pavement and mossy wall, swelling your bread, rotting your crops, thriving in your wetness. That is why you find us so hard to explain.

Maybe you should try thinking all side-branching slantwise, like us: *we* can explain *you*.

*

Description of Archived TEDx Talk on Biomimicry & Innovation, November 202X:

There is a rich white man. He has a sort-of chin and very white teeth: these are the most arresting planes of his face. They catch the stage light as he speaks.

Biomimicry, he says, is creating structures, processes and policies that align with the world's essential design, rather than continuing to hew the old, hard edge of industrialisation into nature.

If nature is a smoothly running organic machine, then industrial humans are a spanner in the works, preventing greater innovation that grows from natural form.

If nature can be understood as a perfectly functioning series of systems that generate and accumulate value, then capitalism, too, is a natural process.

He says you can save the world, be happy *and* make a profit.

Maybe those are actually three different things, but to the rich white man, they are one and the same.

*

Introduction to *Chatting Shit, Growing Roots*, No. 3 ('A Lesson in History'), monthly pamphlet by the NW5 Compost-makers, 25XX:

They tried green capitalism for a while. *Green New Deal!* Investment in renewables, green jobs all round. They no longer wanted petroleum, yet they still grabbed Indigenous lands, cut the trees down and pulled out palm oil, flesh, secrets, took over the deserts as solar farms, blooming hot and bright, dammed rivers for electricity. Everything was switched on. They told people to be grateful: plenty of work to go around, after all. In the bad old days, it was mostly comfortable white people who worked in solar and reaped the benefits of clean energy and shopped at Whole Foods and felt smug about their excellent choices. Then, more and more people had no choice but to work to provide the world with power.

Most people also had no choice about the fact that they still lived in communities thick with dirty air and flushed with poisoned water. The well-off could escape; rich land-owners built eco-hotels for Westerners, running retreats with authentic spiritual practitioners so Sally and Tim could learn how to live in tune with the earth.

The end of the world is over! said the rich and their disciples. What they meant was *their* world was not over, the world of settlers. No alternative forever.

*

Testimony of Fungus no. 2, having lived inside a log and grown words through its gorgeous, pulpy insides [transcribed by Pimsuk Evernia] [YEAR UNKNOWN]:

Once upon a time, work meant breaking people's backs and taking away the bones. Sometimes, worryingly, quite liter-ally. Bones are dry and contained and powerful. People have always wanted the bones of things, have thought up all sorts of reasons to steal and keep the human remains of those who are not their kin. A deep interest in HISTORY or SCIENCE or SPIRITUALITY particularly seems to awaken that appetite—or to provide justification for it.

The white man, Nathan or Jason or something, finds bones very attractive. There has always been this sort of man, but there is a future in which he is more of an obscure joke and less of a clownish threat, risible in his absurdity and might. In this strand of time, let's say a capitalist is something of an eccentric. They take lots of pilgrimages and are obsessed with artefacts of power. They claim to be the descendants of the last green capitalists and love connecting with their heritage, dressing up and play-acting obscure traditions.

John (or Andy or whatever) thinks of himself as agile in body and business. He wears very thin trainers that encapsulate each of his toes and meditates in a shed that he likes to call his office, its walls lined with his collection of bones from all over the world. His favourite is the ghastly staring head of a philosopher that was reportedly displayed in the hall of his ancestor's university. What a guy! Lately, he's been fascinated by other dry, hard things: amulets and talismans and votives that are more socially acceptable to hang around his neck; things that were made from mysterious substances or creatures and worn to attract money, luck, business, women. This is exciting to Matt (or Brett), who dreams of a world with hierarchies and scarcity.

He has gathered similar Thought Leaders in his shed. They are preparing for an expedition, poring over old-style maps and ordering each other about.

One of the Leaders, Adreena, has the same philosophy as Kevin (or Gavin?). She's choosing to agree with him, which means his thoughts are feminist. Adreena is very beautiful. She strides about in high brown boots and a crisp beige outfit, crowned with a pith helmet. It's alright—she's *reclaiming* it. That's how it all used to work in the good old days. It's a sophisticated joke that requires an understanding of the ancient social categories Adreena still identifies and is in fact playing with, and if you don't get it, well—nobody said that *you* were the clever one here. We don't mind telling you that Adreena is very cruel. Ah, problematic! you might say. Surely *he* is the bad one, Adam or Chris or whatever. But Adreena is allowed to be terrible, and she looks great while doing it.

Mike or Bill has dug up an old TEDx talk on biomimicry. He is talking over the man to explain why biomimicry is very important. Adreena nods, adding that women—pause—and people of non-binary experience—are naturally closer to Mother Earth. Naturally maternal, naturally nurturing, naturally natural. Something about the cycle of the moon, the tides, changeability, softness. Harry (Barry?) interrupts her to play a Joni Mitchell song. Yes, it's vitally important to get back to the Garden. Not like this nonsensical way we live now with no clear structural or social division between city and country, man and woman, rich and poor, sick and healthy, good and bad, everyone living all tangled up instead of in the Family, time stretching with the sun's shadows rather than being contained within the clock down to the last second. He can feel that things are going to change, they are changemakers! He starts crying (he is in touch with his feelings).

Are Rob/Richard or Adreena thriving now or languishing in the future? We cannot tell you. Capitalists keep on doing the same thing over and over. It's hard to separate these threads. You might want to poke a little hole in the matted fibres and peer through, but we prefer to follow the strands of knowledge in all different directions at once.

*

'Cringe Incarnate: Neo-Traditional Capitalist Revivals', in *Chatting Shit, Growing Roots*, **No. 3 ('A Lesson in History'), monthly pamphlet by the NW5 Compost-makers, 25XX:**

It was once a concern that ex-billionaires would escape to space. Perhaps that is difficult to imagine since we have long since stopped trying to colonise the worlds above. Some ex-billionaires attempted to live on the moon, but they died in the process, starving or exploding among the stars, and we have to say, it is rather nice when problems solve themselves.

It took the people a while to stop worrying about the capitalists, to relax their vigilance against a class that could never rule them again. It had, after all, taken centuries to lay the grounding for revolution, to birth this new world, and this change did not happen by speaking nicely to the class who would rather die than lose control.

The ruling class were not merely disposed of: their bodies enriched the soil. Eat the rich? Yes, eventually, in a way, once their bodies had been rotted with our caring effort, the nutrients released back into the earth to grow crops or whatever was suited to the particularities of that landscape.

In the place once known as the United Kingdom, the stretch of land from Whitehall to Tottenham Court Road is now a giant compost heap. All the war memorials and statues of colonisers are now dovecotes. We tore down the sculptures and set pigeon houses onto plinths, carved row upon row of holes into old monuments. The birds come home to roost every night, and in the mornings we harvest their nitrogen-rich guano. Pigeon poo transformed the world, and every lofty home for our winged comrades commemorates that wonderful event: the pigeon incident in the insurgency that finally crushed what remained of the British state some centuries ago.

Now there are no more sick feral birds encrusting statues of white men (and the occasional white woman) with white shit. Healthy pigeon guano keeps compost heaps active, hastening the transformation of rotting life. We and all the other gardeners have to fight off the capitalist-cultists who want to try to make souvenirs of literal bird shit; they believe making dung amulets would be a symbolic reversal of what has been expelled from society, bringing back wealth, power and The Market.

*

Testimony of Fungus no. 3, physcia growing slowly and very nicely like lace trim over a seemingly inhospitable metal public rubbish bin [transcribed by Pimsuk Evernia] [YEAR UNKNOWN]:

Lichen is a symbiosis of fungi, algae or cyanobacteria that forms unique natural structures. It was initially thought that the relationship between each partner was mutually beneficial, but it has been found that sometimes it is not, that one can take nutrients from the other rather than sharing. When both parties benefit, the relationship is mutualistic. Attempts to create popular identifications of lichen for the casual hobbyist have, in turn, disgruntled lichenologists, who point out that the initial stages of one lichen may look very much like the mature stages of another. A being that begins in multiplicity is always troublesome.

*

The only post by Tumblr user fungalpieceofshit, June 203X:

You may have heard of a temple in _____ that possesses a pair of nareephon. They are kept in a glass case, shrunken and tiny, little corded limbs like thick dried stems, heads like brown buds laid on a satin pillow.

Say all existence is layered like an onion. This place is a temple in our layer of reality, but, in other realms, the same point on the map is a forest, or maybe it is a cavern, or a palace. The layer we are interested in is the forest. A forest must have a hermit; the wild must have a wiseman who has mastered all knowledge over human, non-human and spiritual life and generously bequeaths that knowledge to the ignorant. Here he is—

The hermit comes across a tree. Its bole curves outwards, branches sinuous and thick with deep-green leaves. Bright-yellow lichen clambers up the trunk and clings thickly to the junction between each branch, in some places resembling velvet frills, while in others it looks uncannily like hair, coarse and bushy, bright as turmeric. He extends a hand towards the lichen, moving away some leaves. A curved body reveals itself to him, hanging heavily beneath the hair. A young woman, he thinks, sweet-smelling and naked, absolutely smooth, like a fine fruit. A wife for him to discard after seven days.

We cannot explain to you how he came to this conclusion. The thought formed within the rubric of his gender-sex assumptions. In this instance, we think it wise to make clear that it is not a helpless girl-creature that he has taken. 'Male' and 'female' are irrelevant to us; there are simply too many ways we like to fuck and be fucked. We are able to form structures that add to the wonders you already know at your point within reality, the forms that you vainly think of as resembling your inside-outside: hair, ears, fingers, nipples, eyeballs, cock, brain. You might understand us as very ambitious fungi that operate between worlds. We like to drop in on you sometimes. Sometimes, you drop in on us, and that does not always go how either of us would prefer.

Now, the hermit brings his new fruiting body to his little hermitage in the woods, laying her on the bedroll, laying himself on top of her. He has been wanting a wife, but his solitary lifestyle prevented him. She sings a little. It sounds like a half-remembered children's rhyme. When he pushes inside of her, she gazes approximately at his left earlobe and continues her song. He cannot remember seeing her blink. The girl-shaped fruit performs no other wifely duties. Fortunately, the needs of a hermit are very simple. An unusual number of edible mushrooms have been springing up around his home, so he doesn't have to go far to feed himself. This continues until the seventh day, when his fruit-wife shows signs of what he assumes is decay, a softening silence. He supposes it is time to dispose of her, but he can't help himself: he couples with her one last time. It is more tiring than he thought it would be to husband his wife. He falls asleep inside of her and dreams she is not a single yielding body but a mass of potential, threading through the earth. It is as easy as breathing to know this and simply become her.

We appreciate the protein.

Nobody really cared about the hermit. Nobody really misses him. The plants and creatures of the forest welcome the sudden proliferation of edible mushrooms in the area, as that means more food for them.

*

Mycoqueer Journal, **No. 78, ed. Pimsuk Evernia [YEAR UN-KNOWN]:**

The idea is this: when a world is empty, it is for the taking. *Terra Nullius*.

'Empty' really means full of water and earth and sky, rich with microscopic life and innumerable plants and fungi and animals and stones and people, so many people, so many homes. To the coloniser, this land is empty. This abundance is wilderness, uncontrolled, unprofitable. This land is pure and fertile, unknown, just waiting for white people to push themselves through the brown earth.

In the centuries after 1492, the Jakes and Jonathans tried to argue that the problem was that this world was no longer empty: too many people, too many things. A world full of waste. Yes, the problem is we want too much and don't share, consumerism is the problem, humans are the virus!

Around the time when green capitalism was beginning to collapse, capitalists started chasing a rumoured place between worlds, an empty space, the kind of place they needed to start afresh. The capitalist imagination accepted the idea of an otherworldly magic forest with ease. Their ancestors, after all, chided other people for thinking there was a Magic Money Tree that the nation state could use for social welfare, knowing well that Magic Money Offshore Tax Havens were the reality.

The entry point to the place between worlds was said to be found among mushrooms. Not a psychedelic trip, but the actual fruiting bodies of mycelia. The capitalists spent considerable amounts of wealth trying to open a way to what they thought of as the other side. Ironically, these mushroom rings only appeared when capitalism collapsed fully and rich people did not exist anymore. But that did not mean the healed world was reset to green rolling fields and pristine forests. No, the healed world is scarred and alive; it has slime and moss and mushrooms and wildgrass and worts and lichen living with trees and bushes and flowers. This is not just about you, a living organism formed as Man with Nature as His Tamed Garden. The spores arrived centuries ago, if you measure time in such a way, and for decades were growing into intricate networks deep in the earth as the struggle went on overhead.

Other than their enjoyment of human-disturbed environments, there didn't seem to be any particular pattern to their growth, nor did the rings comprise any one type of mushroom. Indeed, some alarming specimens pushed themselves up from the ground or through walls and crevices, some of them resembling hands and toes or even heads—this last, most puzzlingly, was accompanied by a halo of particularly fine fruticose lichen that looked uncannily like hair. Mycologists were mystified; they stood scratching their heads by the thickets that border railway lines and popular cruising spots, trying to explain the bewildering varieties, behaviours and relationships between these fungi. But most of them never actually tried to go through the fairy rings. Most of them.

Our favourite was a set of (what you would understand as) gender-anarchist performance oddities, who, after a night of burlesque and poppers, took a nap on a soft patch of grass near us. One of their wigs fell into us during the early hours. Upon waking, the wig's keeper tottered about looking for it, seizing upon the first clump of hair they came upon—only to find themself intimately involved with us. Their friends followed, worried, relieved, awed. They all wandered the forest in their sequinned heels and smeared make-up, enchanted. As far as we know, each person is still here. They all stay by choice. We would miss them if they left.

*

Testimony of Fungus no. 4, the narrative growing from between your toes, in your most intimate crevices, all over your flesh [transcribed by Pimsuk Evernia] [YEAR UNKNOWN]:

Today is the day, wherever and whenever that is. A mushroom ring has been sighted near a temple in _____, a curious fruiting of velvety brown bodies emerging from iridescent mycelia. The signs are all there: Jim (Tim?), Adreena and the rest of the capitalists can make it to the forest realm where everything is untouched and beautiful, a new world just for them.

They go through the mushroom ring to find that the world on the other side is not that different, only there is a thin puddle that gradually widens into a canal, and the buildings begin to break down into the kind of scenery they dreamed about and mourned over: empty shopping malls and broken supermarkets taken over by plants and water. The capitalists follow the trail of shining hyphae that occasionally surface, stopping only for one night to make camp in the ruins of Waitrose. They slumber in the World Foods aisle and feel a deep ancestral connection.

Now, think of a beautiful forest. We hope you are thinking of a place that is abundant, all possible shades of green and brown and black. What you think of as wild has been carefully grown this way, and we are very proud of it.

We want you to picture them: Adreena, uniformed, beautiful, not a hair out of place; Tony or Tom, sweaty and sunburned in his stupid shoes; their acolytes around them, all of them looking up at us in our tree, as they proceed from the assumption that the most important things are at the top and—as they find our shape to be like theirs, hair-head-torso-limbs—that we will be sympathetic to their cause. Our fruit-selves are swaying and humming gently, high in the branches. We are also clustered at the roots, accepting rich sugars and intergenerational memories from our host, giving back nourishment in nitrogen, phosphates and dreams.

The capitalists say, 'You see, our goals are really the same. We can learn from each other and make profit! Doesn't it bother you that you have all this empty land that's going to waste?'

We do not bother replying to such irrelevance. The capitalists murmur among themselves. Eventually, the one in the pith helmet steps forward.

'We declare this land _____.' She does not choose a particularly thrilling name. We know you could do better.

Our contribution is to sing a little louder. We enjoy ourselves thoroughly as the capitalists start bickering below us, making great proclamations of their intentions and doing nothing but argue with each other about their plans. We harmonise with them, which makes them even angrier.

The one with the pith helmet gets out a machete. We do not fear. We will simply fruit again when the time comes, or we will be broken down so that we may nourish others.

The trees' shared memories discordantly ring throughout us, root to root, telling us that we are in danger of something called civilisation. Histories flood into us, not as a steady, shining rill but mud-choked, curled in on themselves like wormcasts, rich as the slime that drips from an old pipe festooned with hornworts. We understand now, yes. You want to clean us up into an English Garden. You call our arrival on the land by the same word as your destruction: 'colonisation'. Yours means the death of all worlds, but when we come, when we grow, all other things can grow with us. We were here before plants had roots. How could you hope to mimic us when we want different things? We digest rocks and sand so the Green can push down into their seemingly impossible surface and draw sustenance. We thrive among roots and branches, our structures interlacing.

We could insist on complex togetherness even if you changed us into your clean-limbed image—we understand this has always been the way for some of you, who have persisted as networks and pods and unions despite all attempts to annihilate your bonds—but that would still give in to civilisation, we have not yet reached that dire stage, we are too wild for bargaining.

We send a message to the Green. The Green arrives in solidarity in all its infinite configurations and formations—whispering bryophytes, winding liana, trees draped in lichen.

The capitalists do not like this. 'Adreena, I'm so frightened,' he whispers, 'I feel I can be really vulnerable with you.' He gropes for her hand.

'Shut up, Steve.' She smacks him away before burying her machete in an advancing column of thick creepers.

'That's not my name.' It comes out more whinily than he intended.

Adreena tries to wrest the machete from dense green but fails. A vine snaps out and wraps around her wrist. 'Shit!'

Not-Steve gently places his hand on hers. 'Listen, it's important. I want you to know who I truly am. My name is—'

A dozen more vines lash around his head and torso, dragging him into the heart of the Green. Adreena manages a quick, cruel laugh before she, too, is pulled away.

*

oh yes we see what you want you want to tear us apart and make us like you, all articulated limbs and KPIs, you want to be the head high above thinking and planning and all of us are four working limbs around a strong core and useful loins that belong to you or we are expelled as shit and piss onto the ground below but you do not see us as rotting down into nourishment only that which is shunned with shame and disgust we are not understandable as hands in production we are infinitely wild, borderless, tangled, a damp patch teeming with sensation, branching and oozing structures, network upon network wet with life. you have already formed in impossible ways but will not admit infinite porosity because you want your body as a fortress, you already break down that which you see as unnecessary and build from its destruction but do not understand decay itself as existence and that you, *you* are vulnerable to it, you are not apart from pain and rot, you loathe those consigned to decay: you see it as punishment, punishment as inevitable, punishment as natural; you do not see how we form ourselves in such a way that we can carefully rot with each other, a network of soft broken bodies that are not broken-as-in-defective or broken-as-in-fragmented but broken-down as in becoming-something-else-always, broken-as-in-porous, infinitely dividing, existing in stretches of time and tenderness.

Push

body   BODY

Push through   body

Swollen / wet / fruit   BODY   BODY

ing   body   body

body   body   body

body

the body is richness itself
give it more body!
the body is a house of abundance
our body
becomes more
bodies to create more
bodies and consume
more bodies more bodies more bodies
more more more more more more
bodies bodies bodies bodies bodies

NO GODS, NO MASTERS.

*

ENDNOTE

A list of things I have knitted (but not necessarily finished) while writing this book, July–November 2021:

1. 3x multicoloured ski masks for art show (variations on Snow Fooling Ski Mask by Megan Swansen);
2. a tiny 'ACAB' banner (art project);
3. a titty top for myself (Ripple Bralette by Jessie Mae Martinson);
4. a mohair top for myself (Ghost Whisperer by Park Williams);
5. a neon-green hat for C. (Best Beanie by James N. Watts);
6. a jumper for myself (Grain by Anna Johanna);
7. test socks for C. (can't decide on a pattern yet);
8. another jumper for myself (Copperhead Tee by Lucia Blackwell);
9. a shawl for myself (A Hap for Harriet by Kate Davies);
10. a green and purple hat for T. (Ava Hat by shinysuperhero);
11. a beret for my mum;
12. a beanie for my dad;
13. socks for K.;
14. socks for J.A.;
15. socks for J.J.;
16. a jumper for J.J.

*

One last story

There is a little wood, a stretch of land between some houses and a school. In front of its entrance is this sign:

CROYDON COUNCIL

*This land is open for public
use until further notice*

Highways Act 1981 Sect.31 (3)

*Croydon Council do not
intend to dedicate the footpaths in
these woods as public rights of way*

*David Wechsler
Chief Executive*

There is a child walking to school accompanied by one of their parents. Neither of the two has any real idea that their usage of this woodland path, strewn with leaves from sycamore and chestnut trees, is contingent on human rules. Each of their existences in Croydon, within England itself, is subject to similar rules, signs, bits of paper, agreements, resentments.

Neither is thinking of that right now; it is frightening, an intrusion. Here there is the smell of sweet decay and growth all around, a place that will rot down and regrow endlessly, beyond the rules of a nation. *Listen*, the parent tells a story. The child listens. Now the child announces they will tell a story, and it is exactly the same story the parent has told, again and again, repeated each day with fresh joy, and it is heard with loving patience. Neither of them has any idea that, in a decade's time, this will change irrevocably. But for now, the parent says *look*, gently holding a sycamore seed between forefinger and thumb, letting it go with a flick so it spirals earthward. The child watches its winged descent, awed.

There are many futures in which this story happens without the sign by the wood.

NOTES

RepresentAsian Mythologies (1)

1   Francesca Humi, 'Exposing the transnational precarity of Filipino workers, healthcare regimes, and nation states', in *COVID-19 in Southeast Asia: Insights for a post-pandemic world*, eds. Hyun Bang Shin, Murray Mckenzie, and Do Young Oh, London: LSE Press, 2022, pp. 162–171.

2   Diana Yeh, 'Becoming British East Asian and Southeast Asian', *British Journal of Chinese Studies*, Vol. 11, 2021, pp. 53–70, https://doi.org/10.51661/bjocs.v11i0.131.

3   Gargi Bhattacharyya *et al.*, *Empire's Endgame*, London: Pluto Press, 2021, pp. 90-92.

RepresentAsian Mythologies (2)

1   Olúfẹ́mi Táíwò, 'Being-in-the-Room Privilege: Elite Capture and Epistemic Deference', *The Philosopher*, Vol. 108, No. 4, October 2020, available at: https://www.thephilosopher1923.org/essay-taiwo [accessed 29 April 2022].

2   Lisa Lowe, 'Transcript: In conversation with Lisa Lowe', interviewed by Luke de Noronha, UCL Institute of Advanced Studies / Sarah Remond Parker Centre podcast, 19 July 2021, available at:

https://www.ucl.ac.uk/racism-racialisation/transcript-conversation-lisa-lowe [accessed 23 February 2022].

3   Tao Leigh Goffe, '"The Other Windrush": the hidden history of Afro-Chinese families in 1950s London', *gal-dem*, 30 June 2021, https://gal-dem.com/the-other-windrush-the-hidden-history-of-afro-chinese-in-1950s-london [accessed 3 May 2022].

4   Stuart Hall, 'New Ethnicities' (1989), in *Stuart Hall: Critical Dialogues in Cultural Studies*, eds. David Morley and Kuan-Hsing Chen, London: Routledge, 1996, p. 444.

5   *Ibid.*, p. 445.

6   A. Sivanandan, 'Hokum of New Times' (1990), in *Catching History on the Wing: Race, Culture and Globalisation*, London: Pluto Press, 2008, p. 24.

7   A. Sivanandan, 'Imperialism and Disorganic Development in the Silicon Age' (1979), in *Catching History on the Wing: Race, Culture and Globalisation*, London: Pluto Press, 2008, pp. 187–190.

8   Zandi Sherman, 'Infrastructures and the Ontological Question of Race', Coloniality of Infrastructure, *e-flux*, September 2021, available at: https://www.e-flux.com/architecture/coloniality-infrastructure/411-239/infrastructures-and-the-ontological-question-of-race [accessed 3 May 2022].

9   Sivanandan, 'Imperialism and Disorganic Development in the Silicon Age', p. 189.

10   Anne Anlin Cheng, *Ornamentalism*, Oxford: Oxford University Press, 2019.

11   Amnesty International, 'The Human Cost of "Crushing" the Market: Criminalization of Sex Work in Norway', 2016, available at: https://www.amnestyusa.org/wp-content/uploads/2017/04/norway_report_-_sex_workers_rights_-_embargoed_-_final.pdf [accessed 24 May 2022].

12   Tamara K. Nopper, in 'Anti-Asian Violence and Black-Asian Solidarity Today with Tamara K. Nopper', Asian American Writers' Workshop, YouTube, 29 March 2021, https://youtu.be/l7MNPXHTowM (1:17:52) [accessed 3 May 2022].

13   Naomi Murakawa, in 'How not to think like a cop, with Naomi Murakawa', *Time to Say Goodbye* podcast, 6 April 2021, https://goodbye.substack.com/p/how-not-to-think-like-a-cop-with [accessed 3 May 2022].

14   Kay Stephens, 'Against "hate crime"', *daikon** blog, via Remember & Resist, 1 May 2020, https://remember-resist.co.uk/writing/against-hate-crime [accessed 3 May 2022].

15   Jun Pang, in 'Abolition: In Defence of Translation | Grounding Practice | Somerset House Studios', Somerset House, YouTube, 9 September 2021, https://youtu.be/-_IcBhRGO3o (15:51–32:27) [accessed 3 May 2022].

16   'Hate Crime & Hate Incident Support & Reporting Service', End Violence and Racism Against ESEA Communities, https://evresea.com/hate-crime-incident-support-reporting-service [accessed 1 May 2022]; 'Third Party Hate Crime Reporting Service Fund: prospectus', UK Government Department for Levelling Up, Housing & Communities, last updated 3 December 2021, https://www.gov.uk/government/publications/third-party-hate-crime-reporting-service-fund/third-party-hate-crime-reporting-service-fund-prospectus [accessed 1 May 2022].

Picking at the Leftovers of 'Grandma's Misplaced Recipe for Cultural Authenticity'

1   Jonathan Nunn, introduction to Claire Finney, 'The culinary lives of our grandparents', *Vittles*, 5 April 2021, https://vittles.substack.com/p/the-culinary-lives-of-our-grandparents [accessed 3 May 2022].

Ancestor, Trancestor

1 Alyson Escalante, 'Beyond Negativity: What Comes After Gender Nihilism?', *Medium*, 15 March 2018, https://alyesque.medium.com/beyond-negativity-what-comes-after-gender-nihilism-bbd80a5fc05d [accessed 3 May 2022].

2 Sophia Siddiqui, 'Feminism, biological fundamentalism and the attack on trans rights', Institute of Race Relations, 3 June 2021, https://irr.org.uk/article/feminism-biological-fundamentalism-attack-on-trans-rights [accessed 3 May 2022].

3 Jules Gill-Peterson, 'The Cis State', Sad Brown Girl (*Substack*), 14 April 2021, https://sadbrowngirl.substack.com/p/the-cis-state [accessed 3 May 2022].

4 the right lube, 'GϵNDϵR CAPITALI$M', https://www.therightlube.co.uk/gender-capitalism [accessed 3 May 2022].

5 Harry Josephine Giles, 'Trans in the UK: What the Hell Are We Going To Do?', *Medium*, 5 February 2021, https://harryjosiegiles.medium.com/trans-in-the-uk-what-the-hell-are-we-going-to-do-73fef741cef6 [accessed 3 May 2022].

6 Craig J. Reynolds, *Power, Protection and Magic in Thailand: The Cosmos of a Southern Policeman*, Canberra: ANU Press, 2019, pp. 14–15.

7 *Ibid.*, pp. 5, 22.

8 Siwach Sripokangkul *et al.*, 'The military draft in Thailand: a critique from a nonkilling global political science perspective', *Global Change, Peace & Security*, Vol. 31, No. 1 (2019), pp. 39–59, https://doi.org/10.1080/14781158.2018.1493447.

9 Teirra Kamolvattanavith, 'No, Thai Dudes Are Not Faking Trans to Dodge the Draft: Activists', *Coconuts Bangkok*, 4 April 2019, https://coconuts.co/bangkok/news/no-thai-dudes-are-not-faking-trans-to-dodge-the-draft-activists [accessed 3 May 2022].

10 *Ibid.*

11 'Transgender Activist Breaks Barriers to Education in Thailand', Thomson Reuters Foundation / NBC News, 18 January 2017, https://www.nbcnews.com/feature/nbc-out/transgender-activist-breaks-barriers-education-thailand-n708366 [accessed 3 May 2022].